JUNIOR CYCLE

CW00670595

LESS STRESS MORE SUCCESS

Science

David Lewis

g **GILL** EDUCATION

Gill Education
Hume Avenue
Park West
Dublin 12
www.gilleducation.ie

Gill Education is an imprint of M.H. Gill & Co.

© David Lewis 2020

978 07171 8977 9

Design by Liz White Designs
Print origination by Carole Lynch
Illustrations by Andriy Yankovskyy

At the time of going to press, all web addresses were active and contained information relevant to the topics in the book. Gill Education does not, however, accept responsibility for the content of views contained on those websites. Content, views and addresses may change beyond the publishers or authors' control. Students should always be supervised when reviewing websites.

For permission to reproduce photographs, the author and publisher gratefully acknowledge the following:

© Alamy: 27C, 73B, 75, 82, 177B, 201C, 203, 211; © iStock/Getty Premium: 25, 27B, 67, 71, 73T, 96, 97, 177C, 201B, 215, 216; © Shutterstock: 24, 81.

The authors and publisher have made every effort to trace all copyright holders. If, however, any have been inadvertently overlooked, we would be pleased to make the necessary arrangement at the first opportunity.

The paper used in this book is made from the wood pulp of managed forests.
For every tree felled, at least one tree is planted, thereby renewing natural resources.

CONTENTS

1 Overview of Junior Cycle Science

Junior Cycle Science consists of the study of five strands:

1. Nature of Science
2. Physical World
3. Chemical World
4. Biological World
5. Earth and Space

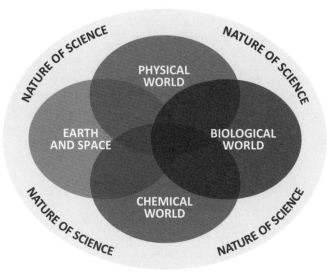

There are three assessment components in Junior Cycle Science:

- **Two Classroom-Based Assessments**, the Extended Experimental Investigation (EEI) and the Science in Society Investigation (SSI), included on JCPA certificate with relevant descriptor. *
- **The Assessment Task** (based on SSI) assessed by the State Examinations Commission, which is worth 10% of the final grade.
- **The State Examination** – a two-hour Common Level exam worth 90% of final grade.

These components assess the 46 Learning Outcomes from the five different strands of the course.

*There are four levels of descriptors of achievement for each Classroom-Based Assessment: 'Exceptional', 'Above Expectations', 'In Line with Expectations' and 'Yet to Meet Expectations'.

The Classroom-Based Assessments

Classroom-Based Assessments	Format	Student Preparation	Completed	Grade
Extended Experimental Investigation (EEI)	A report may be presented in a wide range of formats.	A student will, over a three-week period, formulate a scientific hypothesis, plan and conduct an experimental investigation to test their hypothesis, generate and analyse primary data, and reflect on the process, with support/guidance from the teacher.	End of second year.	Descriptor given by teacher.
Science in Society Investigation (SSI)	A report may be presented in a wide range of formats.	A student will, over a three-week period, research a socio-scientific issue, analyse the information/secondary data collected, evaluate the claims and opinions studied, and draw evidence-based conclusions about the issues involved, with support/guidance from the teacher.	End of first term or early in the second term in third year.	Descriptor given by teacher.

The Assessment Task

The Assessment Task is a written task completed by students during class time. It is not marked by the class teacher; it is sent to the State Examinations Commission (SEC) for marking. The Assessment Task is related to the Learning Outcomes for the Science in Society Investigation.

Format	Student Preparation	Completed	Grade
Students complete a specified written task, which is sent to the SEC for marking.	The Assessment Task will link to the Science in Society Investigation.	Following completion of the second Classroom-Based Assessment in third year.	10% of final grade.

The Final Assessment

Junior Cycle Science has one Common Level exam paper, set by the State Examinations Commission. The exam is two hours in duration and takes place at the end of third year. During this exam students are required to engage with, demonstrate comprehension of and provide written responses to the material provided. The content and format of the final examination may vary from year to year. Every year this exam will assess a sample of the various Learning Outcomes on the course.

Format	Student Preparation	Completed	Grade
Two-hour Common Level exam paper.	Over the course of Junior Cycle, students engage with the 46 Learning Outcomes and a sample of these are assessed on the final exam paper.	June of third year.	90% of the final grade.

2 Nature of Science

> **NOTE:**
>
> Nature of Science is the unifying strand; it permeates all the strands of the course. The elements of this strand place a focus on how science works; carrying out investigations; communicating in science; and developing an appreciation of the role and contribution of science and scientists to society. There is a strong focus on scientific inquiry. There is no specific content linked to the Nature of Science strand itself, and its Learning Outcomes underpin the activities and content in the contextual strands. A knowledge of this will also help in the completion of CBAs.

⇨ Learning Outcomes

ELEMENT: Understanding about science

Students should be able to:

1. Appreciate how scientists work and how scientific ideas are modified over time.

ELEMENT: Investigating in science

Students should be able to:

2. Recognise questions that are appropriate for scientific investigation, pose testable hypotheses, and evaluate and compare strategies for investigating hypotheses.

3. Design, plan and conduct investigations; explain how reliability, accuracy, precision, fairness, safety, ethics, and the selection of suitable equipment have been considered.

4. Produce and select data (qualitatively/quantitatively), critically analyse data to identify patterns and relationships, identify anomalous observations, draw and justify conclusions.

5. Review and reflect on the skills and thinking used in carrying out investigations, and apply their learning and skills to solving problems in unfamiliar contexts.

ELEMENT: Communicating in science

Students should be able to:

6. Conduct research relevant to a scientific issue, evaluate different sources of information including secondary data, understanding that a source may lack detail or show bias.

7. Organise and communicate their research and investigative findings in a variety of ways fit for purpose and audience, using relevant scientific terminology and representations.

8. Evaluate media-based arguments concerning science and technology.

ELEMENT: Science in society

Students should be able to:

9. Research and present information on the contribution that scientists make to scientific discovery and invention, and its impact on society.

10. Appreciate the role of science in society; and its personal, social and global importance; and how society influences scientific research.

Nature of Science

The following pages will explain to you what science is at its core, the role of science in society and how science functions in terms of investigating and communicating. This knowledge will permeate across the four other units – Biological World, Earth and Space, Chemical World and Physical World. It will also help you massively in the completion of your CBAs and Assessment Task.

Where is knowledge of the sciences useful in everyday life?

Biology: ecology, agriculture, medicine

Chemistry: pharmaceuticals, food, fuel

Physics: electronics, lighting, microwaves

Although the above ideas are extremely beneficial, it is important that we as humans are also conscious of the sustainability of Earth's resources (sustainability means the ability to last into the future). Living things are dependent on each other and our actions on Earth have consequences throughout the entire planet.

Lab Safety

Lab safety is extremely important when conducting experiments. It is important that you are familiar with lab rules, safety symbols and equipment.

Rules

Safety

 Corrosive

 Flammable

 Oxidising

 Irritant

 Toxic

 Hazardous to the environment

 Gas under pressure

 Explosive

Equipment

 Test tube and boiling tube

 Beaker

 Graduated cylinder

 Hot plate

 Syringe

 Bunsen burner

 Tripod

 Plastic pipette

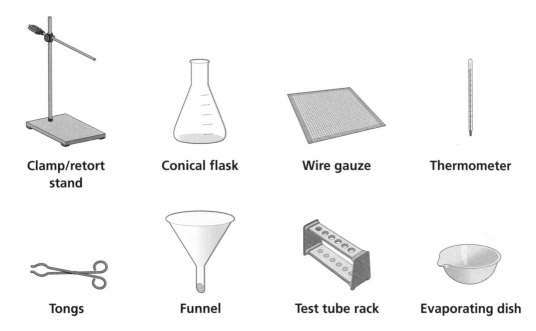

Clamp/retort stand **Conical flask** **Wire gauze** **Thermometer**

Tongs **Funnel** **Test tube rack** **Evaporating dish**

How Scientists Work

key point

SCIENTIFIC INVESTIGATION

Observation	Scientists notice something in the world, *e.g. it is bright outside.*
Hypothesis	Explains the observation and is testable. If expected results are the same as actual results, this supports the hypothesis, *e.g. it is bright outside because the sun is probably out.*
Theory	A tested well-supported explanation acquired through the scientific method of how something works (often modified over time!), *e.g. when the sun is out it tends to make it bright outside.*
Law	A statement based on repeated experimental observations that describes something in nature, *e.g. law of gravity.*

Science can answer many things. However, it is not in a position to answer questions on morality, opinions or areas for which there are no evidence. Ethics deals with these moral principles where scientists ask <u>should</u> they conduct an experiment rather than <u>can</u> they, e.g. animal testing, consent of patient, editing of genes.

Ways to Investigate a Hypothesis

Controlled experiments

- An experiment in which we change one factor, e.g. temperature. This allows us to establish a cause and effect.
- A variable is a factor that changes in an experiment. It may be a cause variable (what we change) or effect variable (what changes as a result).
- Factors that we keep the same in experiments are called constants.

Observational experiments

- Used with phenomena that we cannot control, e.g. orbits of planets. We can still form a hypothesis but cannot change the cause variable.

Modelling

- Models allow us to build structures of things that it is difficult to see, e.g. atomic structure. From these models we can come to understand how certain things work.

Results

- Quantitative data: measured data expressing a certain quantity, data or range and usually associated with units, e.g. metres (i.e. it is number based).
- Qualitative data: data that is observed and not based on measurements, e.g. colour changes or a reaction creating gas. It is also known as categorical data.
- Experiments should be fair (only one variable changed) and repeated (for higher accuracy) with reliable results (similar every time).
- Scientists may then identify patterns and relationships between variables.
- Before they begin the experiment, scientists may research existing data from sources such as books and the internet.
- Information that they have gathered for themselves is called a primary source. Information from books, papers or journals is called a secondary source.
- Once they finish, they may reflect on their methods and results and re-evaluate for future experiments.
- Scientists must communicate effectively with other scientists using scientific language and without bias. Bias is where one side of an issue is favoured over the other and may mislead the public.

Conducting Your Own Research

1. **Research:** Check all resources for accuracy, reliability and bias.

2. **Organise:** Group information you gather and ask further questions.

3. **Communicate:** Make sure your research has answered all your questions and that you present this information to your audience in a suitable, clear manner.

Many inventions have come from experiments and have allowed us to lead the life we live today. They can in turn lead to new inventions. They have a dramatic effect on society, e.g. the Wright brothers' first manned flight.

Accidental discoveries can happen during research and change the course of an investigation or history for that matter, e.g. penicillin was discovered by mistake by Alexander Fleming. The discovery of penicillin changed the world of medicine. With its development, infections that were previously severe and often fatal, like bacterial meningitis and pneumonia, could be easily treated.

3 Guide to the Classroom-Based Assessments and Assessment Task

Classroom-Based Assessment 1: Extended Experimental Investigation

The Extended Experimental Investigation (EEI) gives you an opportunity to research a question you have about some science-related phenomena you have come across in the course of your studies.

It is encouraged, but not required, that you collaborate with classmates, except where it is indicated that students must work on their own. Under normal circumstances each student/group should complete a different investigation.

The process for conducting the Extended Experimental Investigation promotes student engagement through:

- Choice about the topic on which to focus.
- Choice about communication formats.
- The possibility for student collaboration.

The main learning outcomes assessed by the Extended Experimental Investigation are:

Nature of Science	1, 2, 3, 4, 5 and 7

Over the course of three weeks, you will engage in four activities that contribute to the generation of evidence of learning and achievement in the Extended Experimental Investigation:

1. Questioning and predicting
2. Planning and conducting
3. Processing and analysing
4. Reflecting and reporting

The activities are not a rigid or linear process. Each activity may be revisited at different times as you complete the investigation.

You can choose to investigate in one of the following topics:

Water	Earth/Moon/Sun systems	Food	Plant growth and behaviour
Chemical reactions	Plastics	Forces	Energy conversion

You will report your research and findings in a format of your choice. The report can be completed at the end of the investigation. If a typed or hand-written report is your format of choice, the total length of the report would typically be 400–600 words (excluding tables, graphs, reference list and research records), but this should not be regarded as a rigid requirement. EEIs may be effectively presented in other formats, but care must be taken that all the work can be judged on the final product alone. For example, a poster presentation may allow you to show that you can select and present highlights of your investigation, but it may be prudent to include a short written report to communicate any work related to the investigation that is not represented on the poster.

When planning the content of your report, you should be familiar with the Features of Quality used to judge the level of achievement that will be awarded to your work.

Features of Quality for the Extended Experimental Investigation
Exceptional

Investigating
- Forms a testable hypothesis or prediction with justification.
- Describes considerations related to reliability and fairness.
- Outlines appropriate safety considerations, and describes the method used to accurately collect and record good quality, reliable data in a manner that could be easily repeated.
- Uses an innovative approach that truly enhances the work.
- Records a sufficient amount of good quality data.

Communicating
- Presents data in the most appropriate way using relevant scientific terminology and informative representations; calculations, if any, are performed to a high degree of accuracy.
- Describes the relationships between the variables.

Knowledge and understanding
- Provides a justified conclusion supported by the data; identifies and explains any anomalous data.
- Uses relevant scientific knowledge to assess and describe whether the hypothesis has/has not been supported.
- Describes in detail the strengths and weaknesses of their own investigations, including appropriate improvements and/or refinements, or explains fully why no further improvements could reasonably be achieved.

Features of Quality for the Extended Experimental Investigation

Above Expectations

Investigating
- Forms a testable hypothesis or prediction with justification.
- Identifies the variable to be measured and the variable to be changed.
- Outlines appropriate safety considerations, and describes the method and equipment used to collect and record data.
- Records a sufficient amount of good quality data.

Communicating
- Displays data neatly and accurately, using relevant scientific terminology and informative representations; calculations, if any, are performed to a high degree of accuracy.
- Describes the relationships between the variables.

Knowledge and understanding
- Draws a conclusion consistent with the data and comments on whether the conclusion supports the hypothesis.
- Identifies the strengths and weaknesses of the investigation and suggests appropriate improvements, or explains why the procedures were of sufficient quality.

In Line with Expectations

Investigating
- With limited guidance, forms a testable hypothesis/prediction.
- Describes a safe method used to collect data; the steps are understandable but some lack detail.
- Records raw/primary data.

Communicating
- Displays data on simple tables, charts or graphs, allowing for some errors in scaling or plotting.
- States a relationship between the variables.

Knowledge and understanding
- Draws a conclusion based on data collected, identifies some features of the investigation that could be improved and suggests improvements.

Yet to Meet Expectations

Investigating
- Uses a given investigation question.
- Is directed in using equipment to collect and record data.
- Data collection method described is not repeatable.

Features of Quality for the Extended Experimental Investigation
Communicating
• Displays data on incomplete tables, charts or graphs, allowing for significant errors in scaling or plotting.
Knowledge and understanding
• Comments on the investigation without making a conclusion.

✳Classroom-Based Assessment 2: Science in Society Investigation

The Science in Society Investigation (SSI) gives you an opportunity to explore a scientific topic or issue. The development of research and reporting skills are central here, for example searching for information, discriminating between sources, documenting sources used, presenting evidence in a report, applying knowledge of science to new situations and analysing different points of view on the issue, drawing conclusions and communicating personal opinions based on the evidence.

The SSI is an individual research project comprising three activities:

1. Initiating research

2. Communicating

3. Evaluating

You may collaborate with classmates in gathering relevant information and data, but each student must individually produce evidence to meet the Features of Quality of this assessment.

Your chosen topic should relate to one of the following areas:

A technological application of science	An application of science that has an effect on human health
An application of science that has an effect on the environment	An application of science that has an effect on society

The main learning outcomes assessed by the Science in Society Investigation are:

Nature of Science	1, 2, 4, 6, 7, 8, 9 and 10

You must produce:

- A report
- Student research records

You can report your research and findings in a format of your choice. The report can be completed at the end of the investigation or at the end of each main area of activity as outlined above. If a typed or hand-written report is your format of choice, the total length of a written report would typically be between 650–800 words (excluding reference list and research notes), but this should not be regarded as a rigid requirement.

SSIs may be effectively presented in other formats (e.g. posters, podcasts or multimedia), but care must be taken that all the research can be judged on the final product alone. For example, a poster presentation may allow you to show that you can select and present the highlights of your research, but it may be prudent to include a written report of approximately 400 words to convey the deeper research underpinning it. Depending on the chosen format, some reports may involve fewer words, but all the research and findings will be presented using other media.

When planning the content of your report, you should be familiar with the Features of Quality used to judge the level of achievement that will be awarded to your work.

Features of Quality for the Science in Society Investigation
Exceptional

Investigating
- Chooses an interesting or novel topic and research question.
- Finds information about the topic from a large number of varied and balanced sources, and gives a complete reference list.
- Evaluates the reliability (relevance, accuracy and bias) of the sources.

Communicating
- Clearly positions the topic as science in society; explains the relevant science and the impact of the topic on society and/or the environment.
- Presents the investigation in a very well-structured way (that is clear and easy to read), using relevant scientific terminology and informative representations; uses an innovative approach that truly enhances the work.
- Explains different sides of the argument in detail.

Knowledge and understanding
- Views on the chosen topic are considered and discussed in depth.
- Gives a justified personal opinion informed by research, linking the information to the argument and using scientific explanations.

Features of Quality for the Science in Society Investigation

Above Expectations

Investigating
- Chooses an interesting or novel topic and research question.
- Finds information about the topic from a number of balanced sources, and gives a complete reference list.
- Considers the reliability and quality (relevance, accuracy and bias) of the sources.

Communicating
- Positions the topic as science in society; explains the relevant science and the impact of the topic on society and/or the environment.
- Presents the investigation in a well-structured way (that is clear and easy to read), using relevant scientific terminology and informative representations.
- Considers information from different sides of the argument.

Knowledge and understanding
- Gives a personal opinion informed by research linking the information to the argument and using scientific explanations.

In Line with Expectations

Investigating
- Chooses a topic and research question with some teacher guidance.
- Finds some useful sources of information about the topic and gives some references.
- Gives some consideration to the reliability or quality (relevance, accuracy and bias) of the sources.

Communicating
- Mentions in passing the impact of the topic on society and/or the environment.
- Presents the investigation in a structured way using relevant scientific terminology.
- Provides information on different sides of the argument.

Knowledge and understanding
- Gives a personal opinion informed by research with some explanation.

Yet to Meet Expectations

Investigating
- Chooses a topic but is given the research question.
- Is directed to sources of information about the topic.
- Uses very few sources with little evidence of what the sources are.

Communicating
- Presents the investigation using some scientific terminology.
- Presents the investigation in a way that is somewhat structured.

Knowledge and understanding
- Gives a personal opinion without explanation or a link to the original question.

SSI – Choosing the Topic

The chosen topic may be directly related to specific course content or you may decide to study an issue of personal or local relevance provided it is related to the following areas:

- A technological application of science
- An application of science that has an effect on human health
- An application of science that has an effect on the environment
- An application of science that has an effect on society

It is important that the topic can be researched, has a sound base of scientific understanding, and can be turned into a question.

Research should be focused on a response to a clearly defined question. The research question may be revised or changed as the student begins researching for information on the chosen topic.

The above ideas mean that you have an extremely broad range of topics that may be covered. Try to study an area that interests you as you are far more likely to enjoy your research and thus understand it and make conclusions. Planning is critical in science and can prevent more work down the road. As the old proverb goes:

Measure twice and cut once.

One should double-check one's measurements for accuracy before cutting a piece of wood; otherwise it may be necessary to cut again, <u>wasting time and material</u>.

This is critical in your choice of topic. It is certainly possible to choose an interesting or novel topic while not putting yourself under too much pressure in terms of complexity or finding information. A well-selected personalised topic can ensure that all aspects of this task and subsequent assessment flow smoothly and are enjoyable.

Thinking about your topics

In the boxes on the next page, state some applications of science that are relevant in today's world. List examples of how they affect the following:

The environment:	Society:
_____	_____
_____	_____
_____	_____
_____	_____
Technology:	**Human health:**
_____	_____
_____	_____
_____	_____
_____	_____

Choose the two that interest you most and explore how you can deepen your knowledge of them. What else would you like to know about these topics? Note down these questions below. Why does this interest you? Write your answers below.

Topic name:_____

Questions I have:	Why does this interest me?
_____	_____
_____	_____
_____	_____
_____	_____

Topic name:_____

Questions I have:	Why does this interest me?
_____	_____
_____	_____
_____	_____
_____	_____

Once you complete the exercise on the previous page, explore the following ideas:

- You likely already know much more than you think. Ask yourself: what knowledge do I currently hold about this topic?
- List the ways that can you find more information about your chosen topic. This could be through books, online research, conducting interviews, and much more. Think outside the box! The more varied your research the more interesting this will be for you.
- What questions does this topic bring up for you?

Overall topic:_____

Some specific areas I would like to delve into:	**What do I want to know?**
_____ _____ _____ _____	_____ _____ _____ _____

Plan of action:

_____

_____

_____

_____

We all have ideas that interest us. However, while it's fantastic that you have a strong curiosity about the topics listed above, it's important that it fits the assessment criteria.

Sample topic 1:

- Is this topic tied in with the course, your locality or your own passions?
- Are there enough reliable resources available for you to effectively research this topic?
- Is examining this topic really relevant from a scientific perspective?
- Can you look at the topic from a variety of angles?
- Is it possible to boil the topic down into one research question?

When you have settled on your idea, the next task is to come up with a research question. This is a working title, and may change as you learn more about your chosen topic.

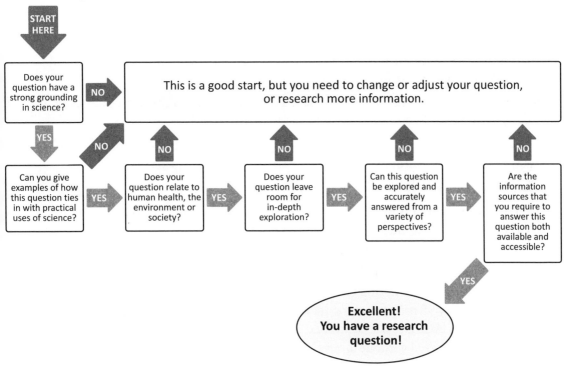

Sample questions may include:

- Should we consider a future of inhabiting Mars?
- Do the benefits of genetic editing outweigh the risks?
- Are electric cars good for the environment?
- How can the ongoing decline of insects affect our environment?
- Does ecotourism truly benefit the environment?
- Can the reintroduction of wolves into Ireland have a positive effect on the economy?

To help you understand expectations of student work, the NCCA have provided samples online which may be accessed here:

www.curriculumonline.ie/Junior-cycle/Junior-Cycle-Subjects/Science/Examples-of-student-work/

The Assessment Task

Students must complete a written Assessment Task for submission to the State Examinations Commission. This will be marked as part of the state-certified examination for Science. It will be allocated 10% of the marks used to determine the final grade. The Assessment Task ties in with the primary aim of the SSI, which is to analyse the data collected, objectively evaluate the claims and opinions gathered, and draw evidence-based conclusions.

Students must complete Classroom-Based Assessment 2: SSI before completing the Assessment Task.

The Assessment Task is Common Level and is constructed with the diversity of the exam students and SSI topics in mind.

The Assessment Task has two steps:

1. **Discussing stimulus material**: The teacher will ask the students to read and discuss the information in the Stimulus Material Booklet in groups. Suggested questions will help to stimulate discussion.

2. **Completing Assessment Task Booklet**: The completion of the Assessment Task Booklet can be done during the next scheduled Science class. This will take approximately 35 minutes of focused work. You must bring your individual SSI along to this class as it will be needed in order to complete the booklet. Booklets must be completed without input or assistance from others.

The Assessment Task will comprise some or all of the following:

- Engagement with a short stimulus in written, audio, audio-visual or multi-modal format in preparation for the next step.
- A written task that evaluates:
  - Your ability to engage critically in a balanced review of scientific texts: evaluate reliability of sources, analyse and evaluate data, information and evidence, and draw evidence-based and relevant conclusions.
  - Your ability to apply what you have learned to hypothetical scenarios.
  - Your ability to reflect on the skills you have acquired throughout the course of the project.

Biological World

Contents

4 ⬡ Cell Structure and Function

➡ **Learning Outcome**

1. Investigate* the structures of animal and plant cells and relate them to their functions.

   *Investigate: observe, study, or make a detailed and systematic examination, in order to establish facts and reach new conclusions.

aims By the end of this chapter you should:
- be able to draw and label a plant and animal cell
- know their components, functions and differences
- be able to describe an experiment to prepare a cell
- be able to describe the diversity of cell functions
- be able to describe cell organisation
- be able to describe stem cells and their potential medical use
- be able to describe ethical issues regarding stem cells

Biologists study cells using light microscopes. Relevant labels and how to prepare a slide for viewing are shown below.

The Light Microscope

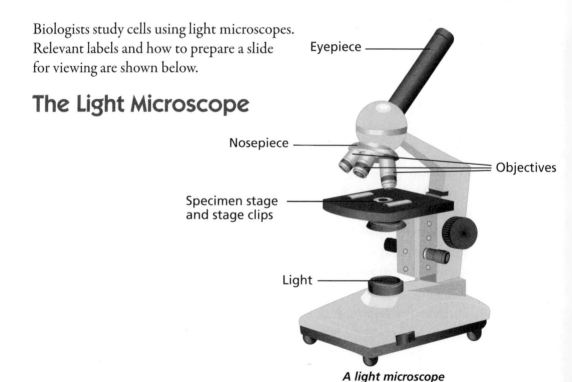

Eyepiece ———

Nosepiece ———

Objectives

Specimen stage and stage clips ———

Light ———

A light microscope

Parts of the microscope

Part of Microscope	Function
Eyepiece lens	Magnifies the specimen
Coarse adjustment knob	To get a rough image
Fine adjustment knob	To get a precise image
Objective lens	Magnifies the specimen
Nosepiece	Allows the objective lens to be changed
Stage clips	Hold the slide in place on the stage
Light source	Projects light through the microscope

Preparing a slide

1. Place a drop of water in the centre of the slide and position the sample on the water, using tweezers. Then add a stain to the sample.

2. At an angle, place one side of the cover slip against the slide, making contact with outer edge of the liquid drop.

3. Lower the cover slowly, avoiding air bubbles.

4. Remove excess water with the paper towel.

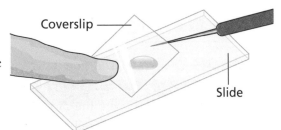

Preparing a sample on a slide

Cells

Cell: Basic functional unit of living organisms.

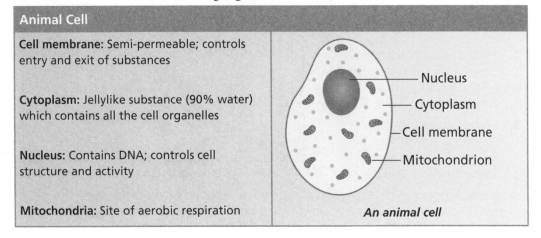

Animal Cell	
Cell membrane: Semi-permeable; controls entry and exit of substances	
Cytoplasm: Jellylike substance (90% water) which contains all the cell organelles	
Nucleus: Contains DNA; controls cell structure and activity	
Mitochondria: Site of aerobic respiration	*An animal cell*

Labels: Nucleus, Cytoplasm, Cell membrane, Mitochondrion

Plant Cell

Cell wall: Made of cellulose; permeable; involved in support and protection

Chloroplast: Contains chlorophyll; the site of photosynthesis

Vacuole: Used for storage of food and waste; involved in cell elongation

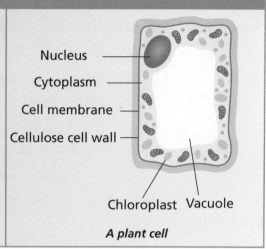

Nucleus

Cytoplasm

Cell membrane

Cellulose cell wall

Chloroplast   Vacuole

A plant cell

Differences between a plant and an animal cell

Plant	Animal
✔ Chloroplast	✘ No chloroplast
✔ Cell wall	✘ No cell wall
✔ Large vacuoles	✘ Small/no vacuoles

Investigate: preparing slides of plant and animal cells

Method for viewing animal cells (human cheek cells):

1. Using a cotton wool bud, rub the inside of your mouth and smear the bud on the glass slide.

2. Place a drop of methylene blue on top of the smear and allow to soak in for 5 minutes.

3. Lower a coverslip slowly using a mounted needle from a 45° angle to avoid trapping air bubbles.

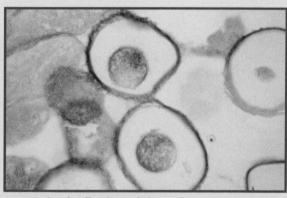

Animal cells viewed through a microscope

4. View slide under the light microscope at (low power) 40X, focus and then move to higher powers and sketch field of view at (medium power) 100X and (high power) 400X.

Method for viewing plant cells (onion cells):

Cut a piece of onion and remove a single layer of cells and place on the glass slide.

1. Place a few drops of iodine onto the onion layer and allow to soak in.

2. Lower a coverslip slowly using a mounted needle from a 45° angle to avoid trapping air bubbles.

3. View slide under the light microscope at 40X, focus and then move to higher powers and sketch field of view at 100X and 400X.

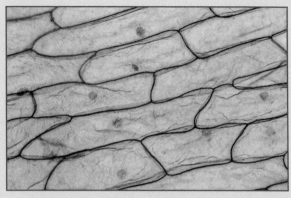

Plant cells viewed through a microscope

Cell Functions

Cell continuity: All cells come from other cells.

key point

Cells generally have the same structure, but different cells have different features to suit the functions that they carry out.

Animal Cell	
Sperm cell: • Tail called a flagellum that allows it to swim • Contains mitochondria in its collar	 *A sperm cell*
Red blood cell: • Contains haemoglobin to allow transport of oxygen • Does not contain a nucleus	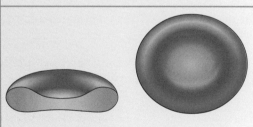 Side view Top view *A red blood cell*

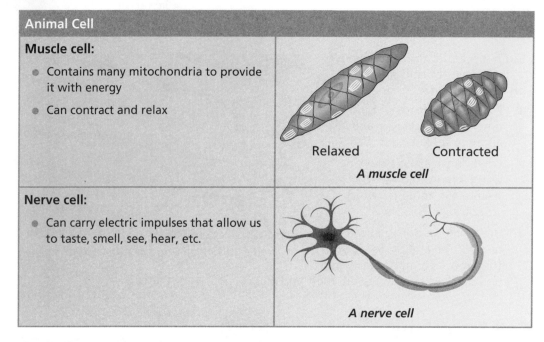

Animal Cell	
Muscle cell: • Contains many mitochondria to provide it with energy • Can contract and relax	Relaxed Contracted *A muscle cell*
Nerve cell: • Can carry electric impulses that allow us to taste, smell, see, hear, etc.	*A nerve cell*

Cell Organisation

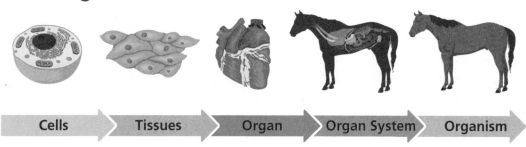

Cells → Tissues → Organ → Organ System → Organism

Cell organisation

Cell: Basic functional unit of living organisms.

Tissue: Group of similar cells performing a specific function.

Organ: Two or more tissues working in co-operation.

Organ system: Two or more organs working in co-operation.

Organism: An individual animal, plant, or single-celled life form.

Stem Cells

- An undifferentiated cell of a multicellular organism that has the ability to differentiate into all types of cells

Found in:

- Embryos
- Umbilical cords
- Adult bone marrow

  (note: adult stem cells are not as flexible)

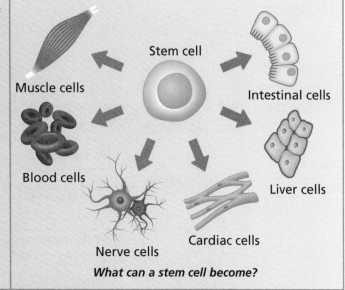

Muscle cells

Stem cell

Intestinal cells

Blood cells

Liver cells

Nerve cells

Cardiac cells

What can a stem cell become?

Medical use:

- Can be removed to form new tissues for grafts
- Research to treat illnesses, e.g. Parkinson's disease
- Adult stem cells used to treat leukaemia

key point

Embryonic stem cell use is controversial as it kills the embryo.

Skin tissue graft being prepared

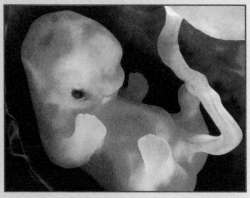

9–10-week-old human embryo

Exam Paper 2019

Question 1

The diagram shows an animal cell.

(a) Use the words listed below to label the parts of the cell.

Cytoplasm   **Cell membrane**   **Nucleus**

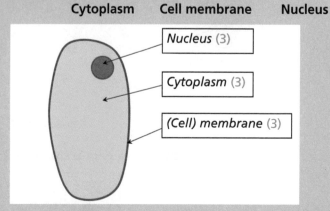

Nucleus (3)

Cytoplasm (3)

(Cell) membrane (3)

(b) Which of the three named parts controls the activities of the cell?

Nucleus. (3)

(c) A student was asked to examine animal cells in the laboratory. Which of the following instruments should the student use? Place a tick (✔) in the correct box.

Telescope	
Microscope	✔ (3)
Periscope	

Sample Questions

Section A

1. What are the terms used to describe a living organism composed of (a) only one cell and (b) of many cells? Give an example of each.

   (a) Unicellular – bacteria.

   (b) Multicellular – human.

2. Outline the function of:
   (a) mitochondria
       Site of respiration that produces energy.
   (b) the nucleus
       The control centre of the cell.
   (c) the cell membrane
       Controls what enters and exits the cell.
   (d) chloroplasts
       The site of photosynthesis in a plant.
   (e) the cell wall
       Provides structure in a plant cell.

3. How is a sperm cell adapted to its function?
   Contains a tail for swimming.

4. Give an example of a cell with many mitochondria.
   Muscle cell.

5. What is a tissue?
   Group of similar cells carrying out a function.

6. Give two possible sources of stem cells.
   Embryo, bone marrow.

Section B

1. Draw and label both a plant and an animal cell.

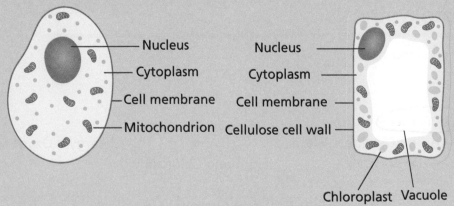

Nucleus — Nucleus
Cytoplasm — Cytoplasm
Cell membrane — Cell membrane
Mitochondrion — Cellulose cell wall
Chloroplast Vacuole

2. Give three differences between a plant and an animal cell.
   Plant cells have a cell wall, animal cells do not.

   Plant cells have chloroplasts, animal cells do not.

   Plant cells have large vacuoles, animal cells have small or no vacuoles.

5 Cell Processes – Photosynthesis and Respiration

7. Describe respiration and photosynthesis as both chemical and biological processes; investigate factors that affect respiration and photosynthesis.

 By the end of this chapter you should:

- be able to describe the process of photosynthesis
- be able to identify the main components of a leaf in photosynthesis
- be able to describe transport tissue in a plant
- understand the factors that affect the rate of photosynthesis
- be able to describe the process of respiration
- understand the different types of respiration and when they are required

There are many processes that occur within a cell. The two main processes that we will study are photosynthesis and respiration.

Photosynthesis

Chemical equation:

$$6CO_2 + 6H_2O \rightarrow C_6H_{12}O_6 + 6O_2$$

Word equation:

Carbon Dioxide + Water $\rightarrow$ Energy + Oxygen

(Light and Chlorophyll)

Light Energy $\rightarrow$ Chemical Energy

PHOTOSYNTHESIS is the process by which plants make food. It takes place in the chloroplasts.

FACTORS NEEDED FOR PHOTOSYNTHESIS

- **Carbon dioxide**: Plants take CO_2 from the air through the stomata on the lower surface of the leaves.
- **Water**: Water from the soil enters the roots and travels to the leaves through the xylem. Leaf veins bring water to all parts of the leaf.
- **Light**: Sunlight is absorbed by the leaf. Light provides energy to produce food.
- **Chlorophyll**: A green pigment found in the leaves. It absorbs light and allows photosynthesis to take place.

PRODUCTS OF PHOTOSYNTHESIS

- **Glucose**: Through photosynthesis, the plant makes a carbohydrate called glucose. Glucose is used by the plant to provide energy for respiration and to form cellulose for new walls. It can also be stored as starch or converted to fat or protein by the plant.
- **Oxygen**: This releases energy from glucose through cellular respiration. It is also released from the leaf into the air.

Components of a leaf

1. **Chlorophyll** – absorbs light.
2. **Stomata** – take in CO_2 and prevent water loss.
3. **Tilted towards the Sun** – absorbs more sunlight for photosynthesis.
4. **Flat and thin** – maximises exposure to sunlight.

Plants have two **different** types of transport tissue.

1. The **xylem** transports water and solutes from the roots to the leaves.
2. The **phloem** transports food from the leaves to the rest of the plant.

Transpiration is the process by which water evaporates from the leaves, which results in more water being drawn up from the roots.

A transverse section through the blade of a dicot leaf shows the arrangement of tissues. Each tissue layer serves a different function.

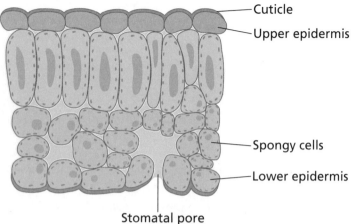

Cuticle
Upper epidermis
Spongy cells
Lower epidermis
Stomatal pore

Transverse section of a leaf

Investigate: xylem vessels

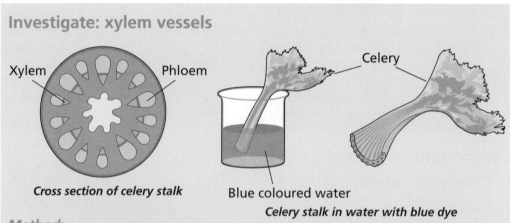

Xylem
Phloem

Cross section of celery stalk

Celery

Blue coloured water

Celery stalk in water with blue dye

Method:
1. Place celery in coloured water.
2. Allow time for water to travel up the plant.
3. Cut plant and note coloured water in upper regions.

Conclusion:
Water has travelled through the xylem.

key point

FACTORS AFFECTING THE RATE OF PHOTOSYNTHESIS:
1. Light intensity
2. Carbon dioxide concentration
3. Temperature

Investigate: how temperature affects the rate of photosynthesis

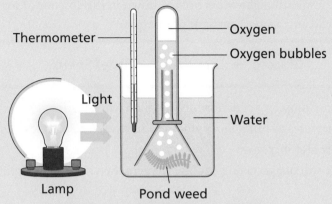

Rate of photosynthesis investigation

Method:

1. Prepare water baths at 10, 25 and 40 °C.
2. Use pond plant for set up to allow counting of bubbles.
3. Count oxygen bubbles per minute for a total of five minutes (more bubbles = higher rate of photosynthesis).
4. Compare different temperatures.

Result:

Photosynthesis rate is highest at 25 °C.

Respiration

Two types of respiration:

1. **Aerobic** – requires oxygen.
2. **Anaerobic** – does not require oxygen.

key point

RESPIRATION is the process of releasing energy from food which occurs in cells inside mitochondrion.

Aerobic respiration

During aerobic respiration glucose is broken down in the presence of oxygen, producing carbon dioxide, water and **a lot of energy**.

Chemical equation:

$$C_6H_{12}O_6 + 6O_2 \rightarrow 6H_2O + 6CO_2 + Energy$$

Word equation:

Glucose + Oxygen → Water + Carbon Dioxide + Energy

NOTE:

Test for O_2 – relights a glowing splint

Test for CO_2 – limewater turns milky

Anaerobic respiration

During anaerobic respiration glucose is broken down in the absence of oxygen, producing lactic acid and **a small amount of energy**.

> Glucose → Lactic Acid + (little) Energy

- During exercise muscles need more energy than when resting.
- Heart rate increases to bring more glucose and oxygen to muscles.
- Breathing rate also increases.
- If muscles are still not receiving enough oxygen, then anaerobic respiration takes place.

Micro-organisms (fermentation)

> Glucose → Alcohol + CO_2 + Energy (small amount)
> (Yeast)

This is also called fermentation.

Factors affecting the rate of respiration:

1. Temperature
2. Oxygen levels
3. Glucose levels
4. Water

Sample Questions

Section A

1. In what part of a leaf does photosynthesis take place?
   Chloroplast.

2. What needs to be present for photosynthesis to take place?
   Sunlight, chlorophyll, carbon dioxide and water.

3. How is alcohol formed? What is the name for this process?
   Through anaerobic respiration in a yeast cell. Also known as fermentation.

Section B

1. How do plants transport water and food respectively?

    *Through the xylem and phloem. The **xylem** transports water and solutes from the roots to the leaves. The **phloem** transports food from the leaves to the rest of the plant.*

2. Why is it important to consume glucose before and after exercise?

    To provide the body with fuel for respiration. It is the basis for respiration and allows our body to make energy, which is used up during exercise.

3. How are photosynthesis and respiration connected?

    Both involve the exchange of oxygen and carbon dioxide. Respiration turns glucose into energy while photosynthesis turns energy into glucose.

4. Explain the formation of lactic acid in a human.

    It is a product of anaerobic respiration. When oxygen is not present the body can still create energy through anaerobic respiration, a process that also creates lactic acid.

Learning Outcome

4. Describe the structure, function and interactions of the organs of the human digestive, circulatory and respiratory systems.

 By the end of this chapter you should:
- be able to identify the functions of the circulatory system
- be able to outline the components of blood
- be able to explain the function of the heart
- investigate the effect of exercise on pulse rate

The **blood circulatory** system delivers nutrients and oxygen to all cells in the body. It consists of the heart and the blood vessels running through the entire body.

FUNCTIONS:

1. Transport of O_2, CO_2, glucose, amino acids, vitamins, minerals, water and hormones.
2. Temperature regulation.
3. Protection through fighting infection/ preventing disease.

Blood

1. **Red blood cells** – contain haemoglobin to transport oxygen.
2. **White blood cells** – fight infection.
3. **Platelets** – clot blood.
4. **Plasma** – liquid part of blood that transports materials.

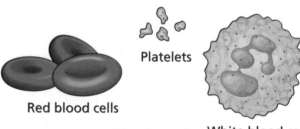

Platelets

Red blood cells

White blood cell

Blood vessel

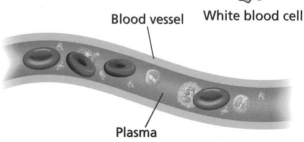

Plasma

Red blood cells, white blood cells and platelets in plasma

Blood vessels

Blood Vessel	Function	
Artery	Pump blood away from heart	Thick, elastic wall — Small lumen
Vein	Pump blood to the heart	Thin wall — Large lumen — Valve —
Capillary	Connects arteries to veins	Single cell wall —

key point

- The heart is the pump of the circulatory system and is about the size of a clenched fist.

- The left ventricle is thicker than the right as it must pump blood around the entire body.

- The heart is made of cardiac muscle which does not tire.

- It receives its own blood supply from coronary arteries and veins.

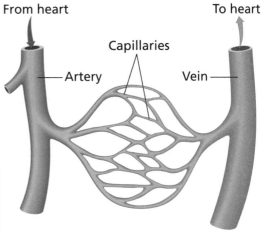

From heart   To heart

Capillaries

Artery   Vein

Artery and vein connected by capillaries

The **heartbeat** is the contraction and relaxation of the heart. While 60–80 BPM is average, this rate can vary based on age, health and activity levels. A **pulse** (which can be easily measured) is the expansion and contraction of the arteries in response to this blood flow.

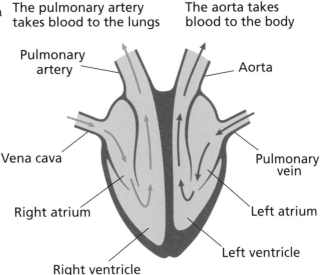

The pulmonary artery takes blood to the lungs

The aorta takes blood to the body

Pulmonary artery

Aorta

Vena cava

Pulmonary vein

Right atrium

Left atrium

Left ventricle

Right ventricle

Blood flowing in and out of the heart

YOUR HEART AND EXERCISE

- When we exercise we require more energy. To help to fulfil this need, our heart rate increases to pump more blood containing oxygen and food to the cells.
- The cells use the oxygen to break down the food faster so more energy can be released in respiration.
- The extra CO_2 and H_2O produced during respiration need to be removed from the body and so the heart pumps faster to excrete them.

Investigate: the effect of exercise on pulse rate

Method:

1. Measure pulse rate per minute by placing two fingers on the wrist and counting the number of beats for 20 seconds. Multiply this by three. Repeat this three times and get the average **resting** pulse rate.
2. Perform exercise for one minute, e.g. one minute of jumping jacks.
3. Measure pulse rate per minute and compare with resting pulse rate.

Result:

Pulse rate will have increased significantly.

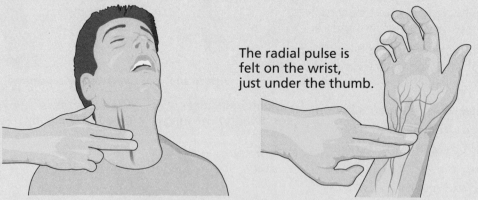

The radial pulse is felt on the wrist, just under the thumb.

The pulse can be felt in the neck and the wrist

Double Circulatory System

Mammals have a **double circulatory system**; one circuit links the heart and lungs; the other circuit links the heart with the rest of the body.

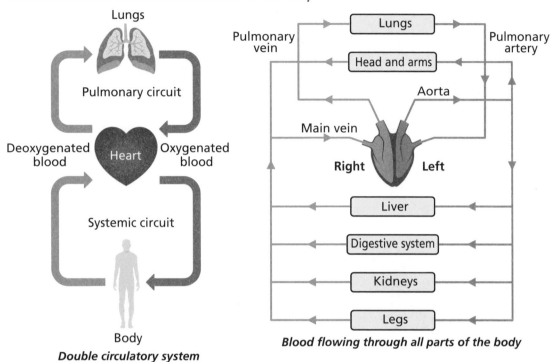

Double circulatory system

Blood flowing through all parts of the body

Advantage: Quick delivery of O_2, quick removal of CO_2.

The circulatory system interacts with every system in the body.

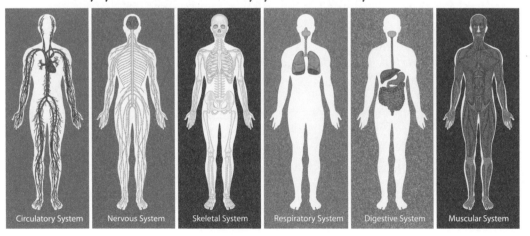

The systems of the body

Heart Health

If an artery becomes clogged, this can seriously strain the heart. If the blockage is in a coronary artery, it can cause a heart attack. If it is in an artery transporting blood to the brain, this may cause a stroke. Therefore, it is very important to have a healthy heart.

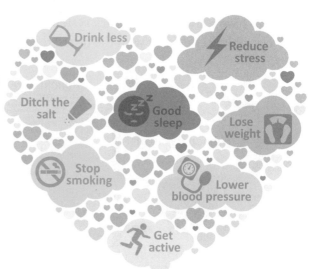

Drink less

Reduce stress

Ditch the salt

Good sleep

Lose weight

Stop smoking

Lower blood pressure

Get active

Tips for a healthy heart

Exam Paper 2019

Question 12

(f) The chamber of the heart marked X pumps blood around the body and generates a pulse.

Name chamber X.

Explain why some of the tubes connected to the heart are coloured red and some of them are coloured blue.

X = left ventricle. (3)

Red = oxygenated. Blue = deoxygenated. (3)

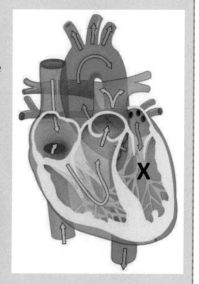

Sample Questions

Section A

1. Describe the functions of red and white blood cells.

    Red = carry oxygen.
    White = fight infection.

2. Give two differences between arteries and veins.

    Arteries carry blood away from the heart while veins carry blood to the heart.
    Veins have valves while arteries have no valves.

3. What is the pulse?

    The expansion and contraction of the arteries in response to blood flow.

4. What is double circulation in a mammal?

    One circuit links the heart and lungs. The other circuit links the heart with the rest of the body.

5. How does oxygen get from the atmosphere to the blood?

    Through the lungs to the capillaries.

6. What type of muscle is the heart?

    Cardiac.

7. Where does the heart get its blood supply from?

    From the coronary arteries.

Section B

1. How does the circulatory system play a role in respiration?

    The heart pumps oxygenated blood around the body to the mitochondria.
    Oxygen is needed for respiration and carried by red blood cells.

7 The Digestive System

➡ Learning Outcome

4. Describe the structure, function and interactions of the organs of the human digestive, circulatory and respiratory systems.

 By the end of this chapter you should:

- be able to identify and explain the different parts and processes of the digestive system
- compare physical and chemical digestion
- be able to describe the functions of teeth in digestion
- be able to discuss amylase action on starch

The Digestive System

- **Mouth:** Chemical digestion (amylase) and physical digestion (teeth).

  ↓

- **Oesophagus:** Carries food to stomach by waves of muscular contractions, i.e. peristalsis.

  ↓

- **Stomach:** Food churned and mixed with juices. Hydrochloric acid in stomach assists in food breakdown and kills harmful micro-organisms.

  ↓

- **Small intestine:** Digestion completed and nutrients absorbed into bloodstream.

  ↓

- **Large intestine:** Absorbs water and stores waste and bacteria.

  ↓

- **Rectum:** Stores faeces in the body.

  ↓

- **Anus:** Faeces exits the body here.

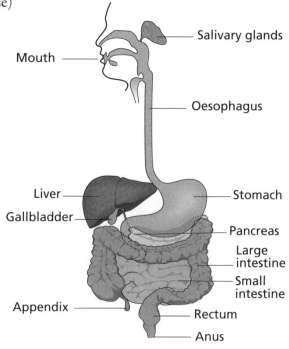

The digestive system

- **Liver:** Produces bile, processes food.
- **Gallbladder:** Stores bile.
- **Pancreas:** Produces digestive enzymes.
- **Appendix:** No function.

key point

The **DIGESTIVE SYSTEM** is a group of **organs** working together to convert food into energy and basic nutrients to feed the entire body. Food passes through a long tube inside the body known as the alimentary canal.

The Stages of Digestion

1. **Ingestion:** Taking food/fluids into the body.
2. **Digestion:** Breaking down food into small molecules that the body can use.
3. **Absorption:** Digested food taken into the bloodstream through villi and carried to the cells where it is used.
4. **Assimilation:** Use of food molecules.
5. **Egestion:** Undigested food passed out, aided by fibre.

Physical vs Chemical

- **Physical digestion** involves mechanically breaking the food into smaller pieces. **Mechanical digestion** begins in the mouth as the food is chewed.
- **Chemical digestion** involves breaking down the food into simpler nutrients that can be used by the cells. Chemical digestion begins in the mouth when food mixes with saliva.
  - Protein is broken down into amino acids.
  - Fat is broken down into fatty acids and glycerol.
  - Carbohydrate is broken down into glucose (i.e. disaccharides and complex carbohydrates broken down into monosaccharides for absorption).

The Mouth – Teeth and Enzymes

- **Incisors:** Flat and sharp used for cutting food.
- **Canines:** Pointed tops that allow for tearing.
- **Premolars:** Crushing and grinding.
- **Molars:** Crushing and grinding.

NOTE:
An adult human has 32 teeth.

Teeth	Specific Enzymes
No chemical change	Chemical change

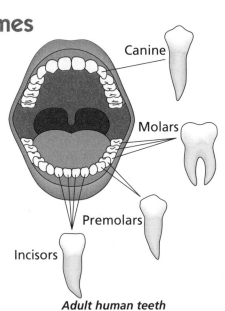

Adult human teeth

Digestion begins in the mouth. The teeth assist with mechanical digestion. Enzymes help with chemical breakdown. Enzymes are proteins that speed up chemical reactions in the body, without being used up or altered in the process. For example, salivary amylase is an enzyme that breaks down complex carbohydrates.

Investigate: the action of amylase on starch

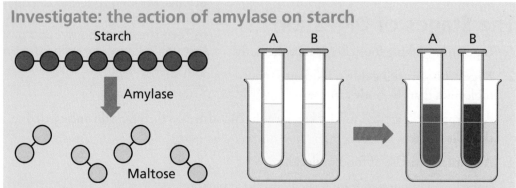

Amylase breaks starch down to maltose   Colour changes indicating the presence of starch

Iodine turns blue-black in the presence of starch. Using iodine, we can show the effects of amylase on starch.

Method:

1. Add equal amounts of a starch solution to two test tubes.
2. Add salivary amylase to test tube A, mix and leave both tubes in a water bath for 10 minutes at 37 °C.
3. Add a few drops of iodine solution to each test tube.

Results:

The contents of test tube A turn red/yellow in colour, showing that amylase has converted starch to a simple sugar. Test tube B maintains its blue colour, showing starch is still present.

Villi (small intestine)

Villi are many small folds that cover the inside wall of the small intestine. They have very thin walls and absorb substances, such as glucose, into the bloodstream.

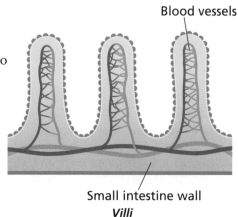

Blood vessels

Small intestine wall
Villi

Sample Paper 2019

Question 4

The passage below explains how a cell gets the materials it needs for respiration. The names of five parts of the body are missing from the passage.

Here are the missing body parts:

Heart   Veins   Small intestine   Stomach   Lungs

In the spaces provided, write the names of the missing body parts.

> When we breathe we draw air into our lungs where the oxygen in the air is passed into our blood.
>
> After we swallow food it is first stored in our stomach for a few hours, where some digestion occurs. Then it travels on to our small intestine where further digestion happens and glucose and other nutrients are absorbed into our blood.
>
> Blood is pumped around the body by our heart. The blood travels through arteries and capillaries to all the cells in our body. The blood then travels back through our veins.

Sample Questions

Section A

1. How is the small intestine adapted to its function?
   Contains villi for absorption.

2. Apart from the mouth, where else in the body is there an example of both physical and chemical digestion?
   Stomach.

3. Name and give the function of two types of teeth.
   Molar – crushing food.

   Canine – tearing food.

4. What is the function of the liver?
   Produces bile: a fluid that assists with the digestion of lipids in the small intestine.

Section B

1. (a) The organ that pumps the blood around the body is shown below. Name this organ.

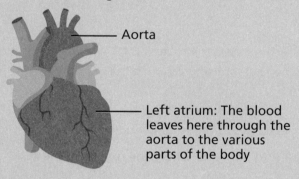

Aorta

Left atrium: The blood leaves here through the aorta to the various parts of the body

The heart

(b) Construct a diagram/drawing to represent the journey taken by a litre of blood from when it leaves the Left Atrium until it eventually returns to the Left Atrium having visited the digestive and respiratory systems. Label your diagram and include in the labelling the names of the substances picked up and discharged at these locations.

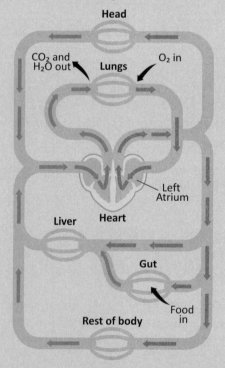

2. The diagram below shows a model of the system which is used to circulate blood around the body.

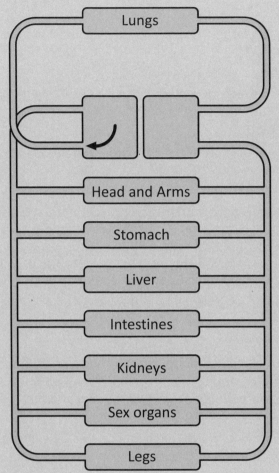

(a) Name the organ that is responsible for pumping blood around the body.

Heart.

(b) An arrow is drawn in the diagram to indicate the direction in which blood flows in that part of the system. Draw arrows in other parts of the diagrams to indicate the direction in which blood flows in other parts of the system.

Arrows clockwise and through each organ.

(c) Mark with the letter **G** a place in the system where the blood gains oxygen.

G at lungs.

(d) Mark with the letter **L** a place in the system where the blood loses oxygen.

L at legs.

(e) Mark with the letter **W** a place in the system where waste is removed from the blood.

W at kidneys.

(f) Mark with the letter **N** a place in the system where the blood absorbs nutrients.

N at intestines.

(g) Describe one function of the circulatory system other than the transport of substances around the body.

Clots cuts using platelets in the blood.

(h) The body needs both nutrients and oxygen for a process called respiration. Describe what happens during respiration and why this proves it is important for living things.

The body turns glucose and oxygen into CO_2, H_2O and, most importantly, energy. This provides the body with energy to live.

(i) Mark with the letter **P** a place in the system where a person's pulse could be measured.

P at head and arms.

(j) Explain why a person's pulse might increase while they are exercising.

During exercise, they would need more oxygen for respiration. To allow for this their breathing rate would increase and then their heart rate to pump the oxygen around the body.

(k) Name one lifestyle choice that could cause a person's resting pulse to increase over time.

Smoking.

8 The Respiratory System

⇨ **Learning Outcome**

4. Describe the structure, function and interactions of the organs of the human digestive, circulatory and respiratory systems.

aims By the end of this chapter you should:
- be able to analyse the functions and components of the respiratory system
- consider gas exchange and its impact on the body
- be able to describe negative aspects of poor respiratory system health

key point

The function of the respiratory system is to exchange gases (i.e. provide oxygen and remove carbon dioxide and water vapour) with the circulatory system.

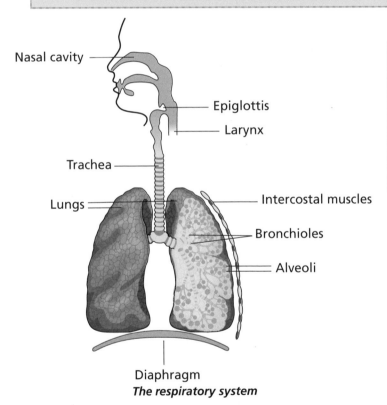

Nasal cavity

Epiglottis

Larynx

Trachea

Lungs

Intercostal muscles

Bronchioles

Alveoli

Diaphragm

The respiratory system

Components	Function
Nasal cavity	Exchange gases and filter out dust particles
Epiglottis	Prevents food from flowing into the trachea
Larynx (voice box)	Vocal cords produce sound as air diffuses through

Components	Function
Trachea and bronchi	Bring gas to and from lungs. Cilia trap dust and prevent it from going into the lungs
Lungs	Contain bronchioles and alveoli
Bronchioles	Carry air to the alveoli
Alveoli	Allow exchange of gases between respiratory system
Diaphragm	Muscle that contracts and draws air into the lungs
Intercostal muscles	Contract and move ribs up and out during inhalation

Inhalation

- Provides body with oxygen.
- Air is sucked in through the nose/mouth.
- Intercostal muscles contract and ribs move up and out.
- Diaphragm contracts and moves down.
- Pressure decreases, volume increases.

Exhalation

- Removes carbon dioxide and water vapour.
- Diaphragm relaxes and moves up.
- Intercostal muscles relax and ribs move back into position.
- Air is pushed out of the lungs.
- Pressure increases, volume decreases.

Gas Exchange

- Capillaries surround alveoli and help in the exchange of gases between the lungs and the blood.
- Alveoli are adapted for gaseous exchange as they are numerous, have thin walls and offer a rich blood supply.

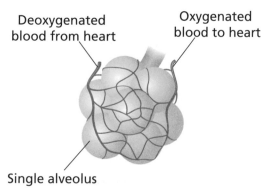

Deoxygenated blood from heart

Oxygenated blood to heart

Single alveolus

Capillaries surrounding an alveolus

key point

Haemoglobin in red blood cells picks up the oxygen that is diffused from the alveoli into the blood.

Carbon dioxide and water are waste products made from aerobic respiration that are passed back into the alveoli to be exhaled.

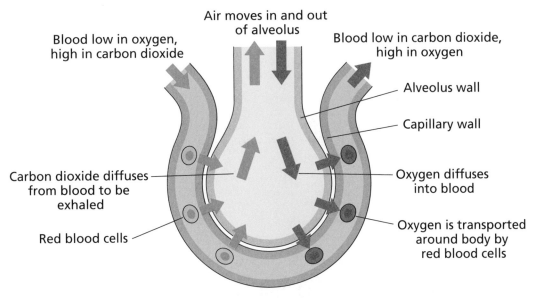

Air moves in and out of alveolus

Blood low in oxygen, high in carbon dioxide

Blood low in carbon dioxide, high in oxygen

Alveolus wall

Capillary wall

Carbon dioxide diffuses from blood to be exhaled

Oxygen diffuses into blood

Red blood cells

Oxygen is transported around body by red blood cells

Gas exchange in an alveolus

The Respiratory System and Health

Smoking

- Smoking is the main cause of lung cancer.
- There are over 4,000 chemicals in tobacco smoke.

Asthma

- Airways react negatively to cold air or dust.
- Reaction leads to muscles tightening in airways.
- Lining becomes swollen and produces mucus.
- Constricts air flow in and out of the body.
- Bronchodilators can be used to treat asthma.

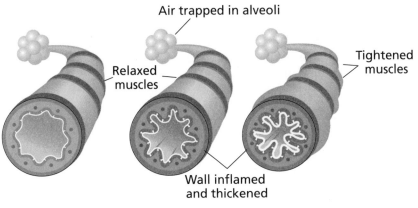

Air trapped in alveoli

Relaxed muscles

Tightened muscles

Wall inflamed and thickened

Normal airway   **Asthmatic airway**   **Asthmatic airway during attack**

Asthmatic airways

Exam Paper 2019

Question 9

The diagram shows the human respiratory system.

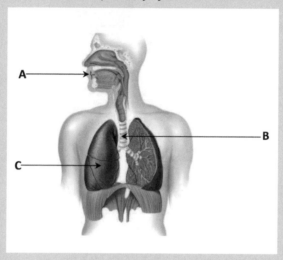

(a) Complete the table below by matching the words to the letters in the diagram.

Lung   Trachea   Liver   Oesophagus   Mouth

Letter	Part of respiratory system
A	*Mouth* (2)
B	*Trachea* (2)
C	*Lung* (2)

(b) Describe what happens in the respiratory system when a person breathes in.

Diaphragm contracts/lowers, intercostal muscles contract/ribcage rises, lungs expand, air taken in, air travels through trachea, oxygen leaves lungs/enters blood/gaseous exchange, carbon dioxide leaves blood/enters lungs.
(Any three points needed, 3 marks each)

Sample Questions

Section A

1. Outline the function of the following structures in the respiratory system:

    (a) hairs in the nose
    Filter incoming air from dust or harmful organisms.

    (b) cartilage in the trachea
    Rings of cartilage help support the trachea.

    (c) moist alveoli
    Allow for better diffusion of oxygen.

    (d) ribs surrounding the lungs
    Ribs protect the lungs from damage.

2. Describe how the respiratory system prevents food from going into the airways.

    When we swallow, the epiglottis closes over the trachea preventing food entering airways.

Section B

1. Draw a diagram of an alveolus exchanging gases with the bloodstream.

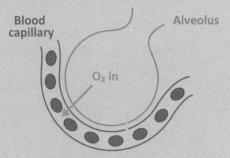

2. Describe what happens when somebody suffers an asthma attack.

    Airways become swollen and produce thicker mucus making it harder for air to travel through the lungs.

9 Reproduction and Genetics

Learning Outcome

2. Describe asexual and sexual reproduction; explore patterns in the inheritance and variation of genetically controlled characteristics.

aims By the end of this chapter you should:
- be able to describe reproduction in multicellular organisms
- be able to identify differences in sexual and asexual reproductions in plants
- be able to explain genetic inheritance in sexual reproduction
- formulate an understanding of dominant and recessive genes

Reproduction in Multicellular Organisms

Sexual reproduction in animals

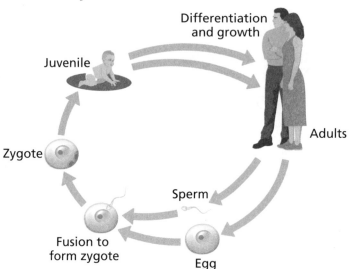

Sexual reproduction in humans

- **Gamete**: Male and female sex cells.
- **Zygote**: New cell formed by the fusion of male and female gametes (a process known as fertilisation).
- **Embryo**: Formed as the zygote divides and grows by a process of cell division known as mitosis.

This type of reproduction produces variation in offspring.

Sexual reproduction in plants

- Flowering plants reproduce sexually by producing seeds.
- Male and female gametes are required to produce seeds.

Asexual reproduction in plants

- No gametes.
- Involves only one parent.
- Parent plants produce small plantlets on stem-like structures called runners.
- These plants are clones of their parent.

exam focus

Know the significance of a plant being reproduced asexually.

Genetic Inheritance in Sexual Reproduction

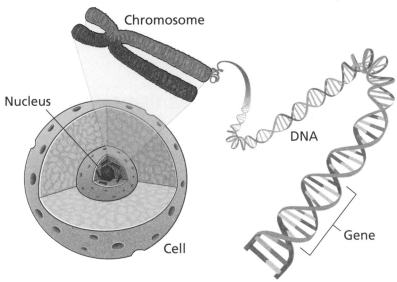

Chromosome

Nucleus

DNA

Gene

Cell

The structure of chromosomes within the nucleus of the cell

Genetics is the study of heredity.

DNA

- Stands for deoxyribonucleic acid.
- Consists of two strands that wind around each other like a twisted ladder (known as double helix structure).
- James Watson and Francis Crick discovered the structure of DNA in 1953.
- The working parts of the DNA are the four bases Adenine, Thymine, Guanine and Cytosine.

Chromosomes

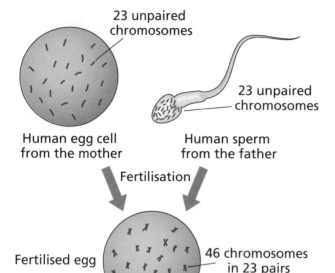

23 unpaired chromosomes

Human egg cell from the mother

23 unpaired chromosomes

Human sperm from the father

Fertilisation

Fertilised egg

46 chromosomes in 23 pairs

key point

Male sperm and female eggs contain 23 chromosomes each, and when they fuse during fertilisation the new zygote has 46 chromosomes.

Chromosomes fusing during fertilisation

- Found in the nucleus of the cell.
- Determine our characteristics.
- Humans have 46 chromosomes (23 pairs).
- Made of DNA and protein, sections of which are called genes.
- Genes contain the code to make a particular protein.
- Genes control the activities of our cells. The genotype is the collection of genes responsible for the various genetic traits of a given organism.
- Genes play an important role in determining traits passed on to us by our parents.
- Offspring are similar to their parents but not genetically identical.

Dominant and recessive genes

- As humans, we have inherited and non-inherited characteristics. For example, hair and eye colour are inherited; the ability to read is an acquired trait.
- Single traits, such as eye colour, are inherited, i.e. determined by different genes.
- We have 2 genes for every trait, one we get from our mother and one we get from our father.
- Alleles are these pairs or series of genes on a chromosome that determine the hereditary characteristics.
- A dominant gene is stronger than a recessive gene.
- When both a dominant and a recessive gene is present, the dominant one controls the trait.
  - Capital letters = dominant gene (B – brown eye colour)
  - Lower case letter = recessive gene (b – blue eye colour)

- Punnett Square – explores how genes can be passed down from parents to offspring.

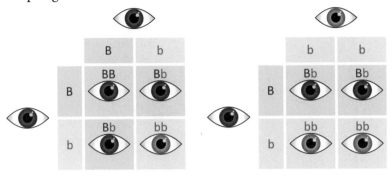

B – dominant brown eyes allele
b – recessive blue eye allele

BB ◉ brown eyes
Bb ◉ brown eyes
bb ◉ blue eyes

Punnett Square showing the likelihood of different eye colours

Variations are the differences between individuals of the same species.

A **phenotype** is described as the physical and psychological characteristics of an organism influenced by both genetic and environmental factors.

Genetic factors

- Mutations that cause disease, e.g. cystic fibrosis
- Fertilisation

Environmental factors

- Diet
- Lifestyle
- Climate

Exam Paper 2019

Question 5

(c) Suffering from sickle cell anaemia is an example of a genetically controlled characteristic. Classify the characteristics below as being either genetically controlled or not genetically controlled by placing a tick in the correct column in each case.

Characteristic	Genetically controlled	Not genetically controlled
Eye colour	✔ (3)	
How to cycle a bike		✔ (3)

Question 14

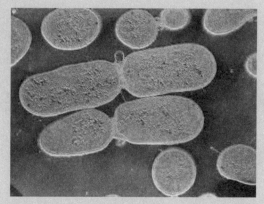

(g) The image shows bacterial cells dividing in order to reproduce. This is an example of asexual reproduction.

Describe one difference between sexual and asexual reproduction.

Sexual reproduction – offspring not genetically identical.

Asexual reproduction – offspring genetically identical. (3)

Sample Questions

Section A

1. Explain how a zygote develops into a new individual.

    It develops by mitosis until it becomes an embryo and then a foetus which grows into a baby.

2. Explain why offspring resulting from sexual reproduction are similar to their parents but not identical to them.

    They are a mixture of genes from both the mother and father.

3. Explain the difference between recessive and dominant genes.

    Two recessive genes must be present for a trait to be expressed whereas only one dominant gene must be present as it masks a recessive gene.

4. In humans the gene for green eyes, G, is dominant over the gene for grey eyes, g. What colour eyes would a person have if their two genes for eye colour were:

    (a) GG   (b) Gg   (c) gg

    Green.   *Green.*   *Grey.*

Section B

1. During sexual reproduction each parent passes on only half of their chromosomes to each of their offspring. Why is this necessary?

    To allow for variation in a species.

2. Draw Punnett squares for the following combinations of male and female gametes, where B stands for brown eye colour and b for blue eye colour.

    (a) Male gamete = Bb, female gamete = BB

    Bb × BB.

Gametes	B	b
B	BB	Bb
B	BB	Bb

    (b) Male gamete = Bb, female gamete = Bb

    Bb × Bb.

Gametes	B	b
B	BB	Bb
b	Bb	bb

    (c) In each case, what is the likeliness that the offspring will have the genes bb?

    a – 0% b – 25%.

10 Reproduction in Humans

Learning Outcome

9. Explain human sexual reproduction; discuss medical, ethical and societal issues.

By the end of this chapter you should:
- be able to identify relevant parts and events in the male and female reproductive systems
- be able to outline sexual reproduction and pregnancy
- be able to describe the various stages of the birthing process
- be able to discuss family planning and issues regarding pregnancy

The Female Reproductive System
- **Ovary:** Contains eggs.
- **Fallopian tube:** Carries egg to the uterus.

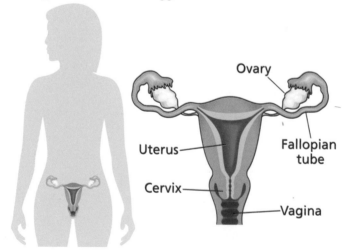

Ovary

Uterus

Fallopian tube

Cervix

Vagina

Female reproductive system

- **Uterus:** Fertilised egg develops into a baby.
- **Vagina:** During sexual intercourse, the penis is placed in the vagina, so that sperm can be released. Also acts as the birth canal during pregnancy.

The menstrual cycle

- Series of changes that take place in the female reproductive system to allow for the possibility of pregnancy.
    - Days 1–5: Lining of uterus sheds/menstruation occurs.
    - Days 6–13: The lining of the womb builds up.
    - Day 14: Ovulation occurs – the egg is released from the ovary.
    - Days 15–28: The lining of the womb continues to thicken. If the egg is not fertilised, the lining and egg will later be shed.
- The cycle repeats.

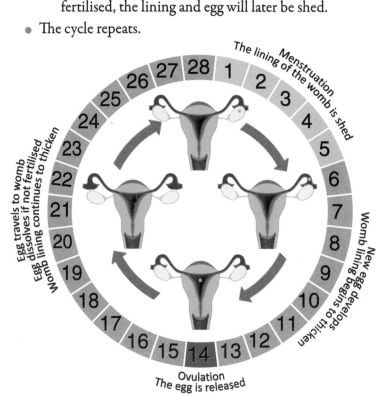

The menstrual cycle

OVULATION is the release of an unfertilised egg from the ovary.

MENSTRUATION is the release of the uterus lining, unfertilised egg and blood through the vagina.

The Male Reproductive System

- **Testes:** Make sperm cells.
- **Penis:** Allows sperm to be transferred to a woman's body.
- **Seminal gland:** Produces fluid to nourish sperm.
- **Sperm ducts:** Carry sperm and seminal fluid.

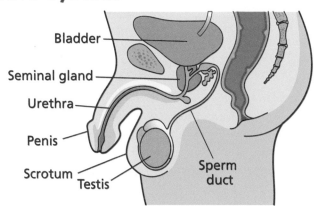

The male reproductive system

Puberty

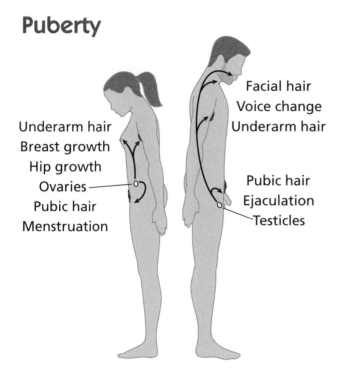

Facial hair
Voice change
Underarm hair

Underarm hair
Breast growth
Hip growth
Ovaries
Pubic hair
Menstruation

Pubic hair
Ejaculation
Testicles

PUBERTY is the process of a child's body maturing into an adult one, capable of sexual reproduction. It is caused by the release of sex hormones in the body.

Female and male changes during puberty

Sexual Intercourse and Pregnancy

- **Sexual intercourse:** When the erect penis of the man is placed in the woman's vagina. Movement of the penis in the vagina causes semen, containing sperm, to be released.
- **The fertile period:** The time during the menstrual cycle when sexual intercourse is most likely to result in a pregnancy. Females are most fertile within a day or two of ovulation.

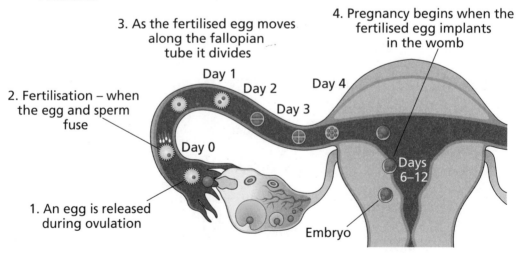

3. As the fertilised egg moves along the fallopian tube it divides

4. Pregnancy begins when the fertilised egg implants in the womb

Day 1
Day 2
Day 4
Day 3

2. Fertilisation – when the egg and sperm fuse

Day 0

Days 6–12

1. An egg is released during ovulation

Embryo

The journey of the fertilised egg to the womb

- **Ovulation:** Release of egg from the ovary.
- **Ejaculation:** Release of sperm from the penis.
- **Fertilisation:** Fusion of sperm with the egg (gametes) to form a zygote.
- **Implantation:** Attachment of zygote to soft lining of the womb.
- **Pregnancy:** The period of time the cell takes to develop into a fully formed foetus in the womb, usually 40 weeks.
- **Amniotic fluid:** A protective liquid surrounding the embryo.
- **Placenta:** Allows food and oxygen from the mother to pass to the baby; the baby passes water, CO_2 and wastes to the mother.
- The **umbilical cord:** Connects the embryo to the placenta.

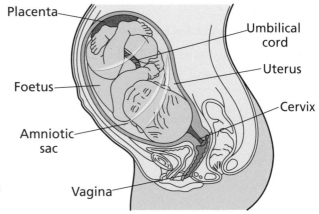

Foetus in the uterus

Birth

Labour:

- Contractions of the muscles of the uterus cause the cervix to widen.
- The amniotic sac bursts and the baby is pushed out. (The umbilical cord is clamped and then cut.)
- The placenta is also dispelled from the vagina.

Family planning

- **Natural methods** – detects the day on which ovulation takes place.
- **Artificial methods** – preventing the sperm and egg from fusing using a barrier (e.g. condom) or using chemical hormones to prevent ovulation (e.g. contraceptive pill).

Factors affecting pregnancy

1. Medical problems can make conceiving a challenge, e.g. ovulation disorders such as polycystic ovary syndrome (PCOS). Women with PCOS typically have a number of small cysts around the edge of their ovaries. They either fail to ovulate or ovulate infrequently, making it very difficult to conceive.

2. A pregnancy may be terminated through an abortion. In the Republic of Ireland, you can have an abortion up to 12 weeks of pregnancy and after that, only in exceptional circumstances.

3. Societal issues such as China's former one-child policy may influence whether pregnancy occurs. This government programme, which ended in 2016, aimed to

limit family units in the country to one child each and, in turn, slow the growth of China's population.

Breastfeeding

Once the baby is born, the mother's body makes a hormone to stimulate the production of milk.

Advantages of breastfeeding:

- Provides extra antibodies and nutrients.
- Promotes a bond between mother and baby.

Sample Paper 2019

Question 7

The picture below shows a human female sex cell surrounded by human male sex cells.

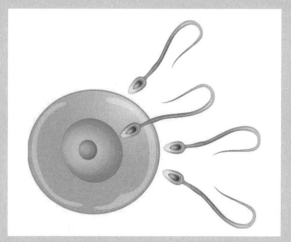

(a) What is the human female sex cell called?
    Egg.

(b) What is the human male sex cell called?
    Sperm.

(c) Where in the female reproductive system is the female sex cell produced?
    Ovary.

(d) In the diagram, draw a box around the male sex cell that is fertilising the female sex cell.
    Box drawn around second sperm down.

(e) State one way of reducing the chance that sexual intercourse could result in fertilisation.
    Use of condom.

Sample Questions

Section A

1. Explain the following terms:

   (a) Gamete
   A sex cell.

   (b) Zygote
   Resulting cell of fusion of gametes.

   (c) Ovulation
   When eggs are released from the ovary.

   (d) Fertilisation
   When sperm fuses with egg.

   (e) Implantation
   Attachment of zygote to soft lining of the womb.

Section B

1. What is puberty? Explain the differences in how males and females undergo puberty.

   Puberty is the period in which adolescents reach sexual maturity and become capable of reproduction.

   Girls: growth of breasts, widening of hips and development of vagina, uterus and fallopian tubes. Menstruation begins.

   Boys: testicles develop, voice deepens and pubic hair grows.

2. What was China's 'one-child policy'?

   The one-child policy was a programme in China that was implemented nationwide by the Chinese government in 1980 in order to limit most Chinese families to one child each.

   Why did the Chinese government want to do this?

   The Chinese government wanted to address the growth rate of the country's population, which they viewed as being too rapid.

11 Human Health

Learning Outcome

6. Evaluate how human health is affected by: inherited factors and environmental factors including nutrition; lifestyle choices; examine the role of micro-organisms in human health.

aims By the end of this chapter you should:

- explore types of micro-organisms, establishing positives and negatives for each
- be able to discuss the immune system and its constituent parts
- understand factors affecting human health

Health: *'a state of complete physical, mental and social wellbeing and not merely the absence of disease or infirmity'* – The World Health Organization

Micro-organisms

A **micro-organism** or microbe is an organism too small to be seen by the unaided human eye. Micro-organisms include viruses, fungi and bacteria.

1. Viruses

- Cannot be seen under a light microscope.
- Small amount of DNA surrounded by a protein coat.
- Attack living cells and use cells to make more copies of the virus.
- Positive effects: genetic engineering.
- Negative effects: e.g. HIV/AIDS.

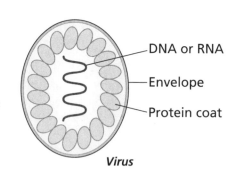

Virus

DNA or RNA
Envelope
Protein coat

2. Fungi

- Can be found in different forms: single cell (e.g. yeast), fine thread (e.g. bread mould) and larger structures (e.g. mushrooms).
- Feed by absorbing food and cannot make their own.

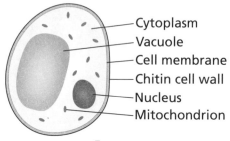

Fungus

Cytoplasm
Vacuole
Cell membrane
Chitin cell wall
Nucleus
Mitochondrion

- Positive effects: penicillium produces antibiotics.
- Negative effects: athlete's foot, poison mushrooms.

3. Bacteria

Simple living cells that reproduce very quickly.

Positive effects of bacteria:

- Help make vitamins.
- Help digest food.
- Production of antibiotics, i.e. chemicals that can kill bacteria/fungi without harming us.

Negative effects of bacteria:

- Cause illness and disease.
- Cause food spoilage.
- Cause tooth decay.

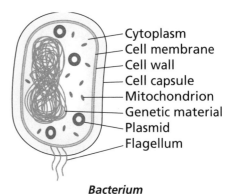

Cytoplasm
Cell membrane
Cell wall
Cell capsule
Mitochondrion
Genetic material
Plasmid
Flagellum

Bacterium

Biotechnology

Biotechnology is the use of living things to produce useful products, e.g. yeast is used to produce alcohol. Biotechnology allows these products to be produced cheaply, in large quantities and without harmful by-products.

The Immune System

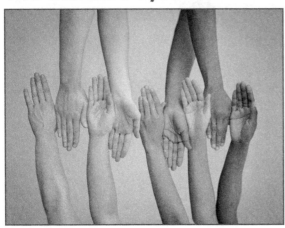

key point

Skin is the first line of defence against infection.

- Acts as a barrier.
- Secretes sweat.
- Detects infection.
- Triggers the immune system.

White blood cells

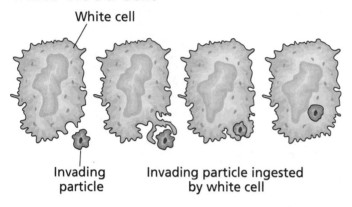

White blood cell engulfing invading particle

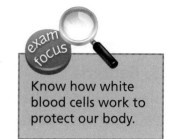

Engulfing – when white blood cells 'swallow' and digest harmful bacteria.

Antibody – A protein, produced by white blood cells, that kills or stops the growth of other micro-organisms.

Immunity – when our body has made an antibody for a particular virus and remembers how to do it.

Vaccines – small injections of weak/dead versions of a virus, letting our bodies learn how to make the antibody for that virus.

Factors Affecting Human Health

1. Inherited factors – genetic illnesses

- Caused by faulty genes.
- Having faulty copies of genes can lead to higher chances of getting some illnesses. For example, a faulty copy of the BRCA1 gene increases the risk of getting breast or ovarian cancer. Cystic fibrosis, haemophilia and sickle cell anaemia are other genetic illnesses.
- Genetic screening is used to test a person's genes.

2. Environmental factors

Air quality

- Burning fossil fuels produces smoke and other harmful substances. This leads to environmental problems.
- Smog can irritate the lungs.
- Bans on burning fossil fuels lead to positive effects on the air we breathe.

Clean drinking water

- Untreated drinking water can lead to the growth of bacteria and parasites. This is a large problem in warmer climates.
- 3–5 million cases of cholera each year.

3. Lifestyle – exercise

- Endorphins – chemicals released while exercising that improve the mood.
- Reduces the risk of type 2 diabetes.
- Reduces chance of osteoporosis.
- Reduces stress.
- Improves sleep.
- Maintains a healthy body weight.
- Improves skin.
- Helps you think more clearly.
- Helps you avoid illnesses.

4. Lifestyle – mental health

- Good mental health can help you:
  1. Realise your own potential.
  2. Cope with the normal stresses of life.
  3. Work productively.
  4. Contribute to society.

Exam Paper 2019

Question 14

(e) Human health is affected by environmental factors such as stress. Name another environmental factor which has an effect on human health.
Air quality. (3)

(f) This article highlights a beneficial role of micro-organisms in human health. [Micro-organisms in the gut produce fatty acids that are important for brain health.] State another example of how bacteria could have an effect on human health.
Food poisoning. (3)

Sample Questions

Section A

1. List two illnesses caused by bacteria and two caused by viruses.
   Bacteria: food poisoning, cholera.
   Viruses: cold, flu.

2. What are vaccinations and how do they work?
   A vaccine works by training the immune system to recognise and combat harmful viruses or bacteria. By injecting a small amount into the body, the immune system can safely learn to recognise them as hostile invaders, produce antibodies, and remember them for the future.

3. What is aerobic exercise?
   Any exercise that increases breathing and heart rate.

4. List three things a person can do to improve their mental health.
   Exercise, sleep, open up to others.

5. How are genetic illnesses different than those caused by bacteria and viruses?
   A genetic illness is a disorder resulting from changes or mutations in an individual's DNA, whereas bacteria and viruses involve invasive action.

Section B

1. List three different ways we can stop food being spoiled by bacteria.
   Salt the food.

   Store in zip-locked bags.

   Store in fridge or freezer (cold temperatures).

2. Describe how Ireland has attempted to improve our air quality.
   By allocating more road space for walking, cycling and public transport. By introducing the smoky coal ban in the early 1990s.

12 Evolution

 Learning Outcome

3. Outline evolution by natural selection and how it explains the diversity of living things.

aims By the end of this chapter you should:
- recognise evolution and be able to illustrate its discovery
- be able to justify the theory of natural selection
- know how to explain biodiversity on Earth in the context of evolution

Species – a group of similar organisms, capable of interbreeding and producing fertile offspring.

- Offspring are similar but not identical to their parents.

 key point

EVOLUTION

The process of change in the general characteristics of a species in response to their environment over a long period of time.

| Mesonychid | Ambulocetus | Rodhocetus | Killer whale |
| 48 million years ago | 43 million years ago | 41 million years ago | Present day |

Evolution of a killer whale

Charles Darwin

- His book, *On the Origin of Species*, was published in 1859.
- Suggests how evolution within a species may result in an entirely new species.
- Species living on Earth today evolved from species which have lived in the past and may still live here today.
- Evolution by natural selection.

Charles Darwin

The Tree of Life

A Family Portrait

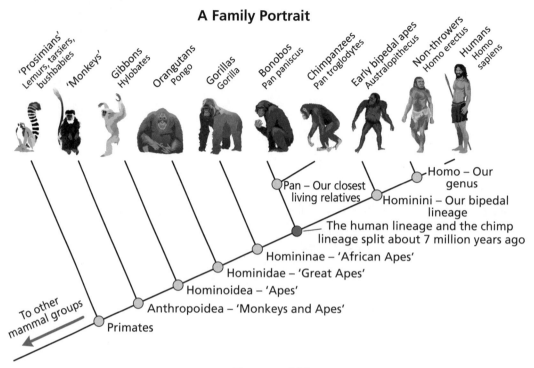

The tree of life

You can trace the lineage of every single species back to the very first living thing. Species that are closely related are found near to each other on the tree of life.

Natural Selection

Variation – the difference between the individuals in a species.

- Sexual reproduction and changes in DNA cause variations among offspring.

Mutation – is a change in DNA.

Inheritable characteristics – controlled by genes and can be passed on from parent to offspring.

NATURAL SELECTION

The process by which organisms that are better adapted to their environment tend to survive and produce more offspring.

- Parents who have adapted well to their environment may pass down these beneficial characteristics to their offspring.
- Over generations these characteristics become more commonplace among the species.

Adaptation – a characteristic that improves the chances of an organism surviving and reproducing.

- Polar bears have adapted to their harsh arctic environment over the generations by developing thick fur coats.

Evolution within a Species

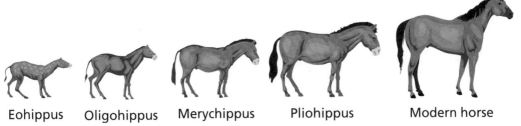

| Eohippus | Oligohippus | Merychippus | Pliohippus | Modern horse |

The evolution of the modern horse

Over millions of years the process of natural selection favoured the faster horses in each generation.

- This allowed them to escape predators.
- Gave them more chances to make offspring.

A new species can evolve from an existing one when they become separated from the rest of the species.

The new environment is different from the old one, causing new characteristics to develop within the species.

Biodiversity

- Life on Earth began 4 billion years ago.
- Conditions for natural selection existed throughout this time.
- **Niche** – a role within the environment.

Exam Paper 2019

Question 14

(h) Over time bacteria can evolve. Outline the theory of evolution by natural selection.

Genetic mutation, variation between member species, overproduction, competition, survival of the fittest, beneficial genes passed to offspring, new species formed/extinction. (any three points needed, 2 marks each)

Sample Questions

Section A

1. Explain how the process of natural selection occurs.

   Natural selection is the process by which organisms that are best suited to their environment survive and pass on their genetic traits in increasing numbers to successive generations. At the same time, organisms that are less adapted fail to survive or multiply at a lower rate and tend to be eliminated from the ecosystem – some are 'naturally selected'.

2. Explain how evolution within a species occurs.

   Organisms with favourable traits are more likely to reproduce and in doing so pass on these traits to the next generation. Over time this sees organisms adapt to their environment.

3. After a particularly harsh winter a population of sheep give birth to a generation of lambs that grow to be significantly smaller sheep then their parents. Does this mean that the sheep are evolving to become smaller? Explain your answer.

   No, it means that the sheep and the lambs did not get a lot of food during that winter and have grown as such. Evolution takes place over a long period of time.

4. Explain how evolution may give rise to a new species.

   If adaptation keeps occurring in a species, they may become so different that they form a new species.

5. Explain how evolution accounts for the diversity of living things.

   Organisms continually adapt to their environment, and the diversity of environments that exists results in a diversity of organisms adapted to them.

Section B

1. As part of his theory on evolution, Darwin suggested that natural selection could occur without causing evolution. Using your knowledge of natural selection explain how this could occur.

    Genetic variation to adapt to a certain environment does not necessarily mean evolution. Already adapted animals may survive without change while the unadapted do not.

2. What do you think this drawing suggests about evolution in humans? Does it fit in with Darwin's ideas about the tree of life?

    It suggests chimps grew into man in one straight line. However, chimps and man both evolved from one ancient ancestor.

Learning Outcome

10. Evaluate how humans can successfully conserve ecological biodiversity and contribute to global food production; appreciate the benefits that people obtain from ecosystems.

aims By the end of this chapter you should:
- identify human dependence on the natural world
- be able to explain the threats to biodiversity on Earth

- Number of species on Earth (excluding bacteria) = 8.7 million
- Number of species in Ireland = 31,000

Sustainability – maintaining ecosystems for future generations.

Ways humans depend on the natural world:

- We use crops to feed livestock/ourselves.
- Bees are needed to pollinate flowers.
- Plants provide us with food to eat.
- Plants provide us with oxygen to respire.
- Recreational activities.
- Fungi produces antibiotics.

Biodiversity is threatened by:

- Modern methods of food production.
- Extracting raw materials.
- Pollution (air, water and soil), i.e. the addition of harmful materials to the environment.
- Burning fossil fuels.

key point

BIODIVERSITY is the variety of living things on Earth.

Biodiversity and Global Food Production

- Population of humans on Earth is to reach 9 billion by 2050.
- We must find ways to:
  — Produce enough food to support growing population.
  — Conserve ecological biodiversity.

1. Land clearing

- Human activity has reduced the forest coverage in Ireland to just 10%.
- 70% of deforestation in the world is due to agriculture.

This threatens biodiversity because:

- Fields and residential areas that replace forests do not have the same diversity of life.
- Agricultural land cannot support the same diversity of life.

Controlling biodiversity through wise land management:

- Governments pass laws to protect biodiversity.
- Coillte (a state-sponsored company) drives the initiative to replant native woodlands.
- National parks.

2. Hunting

Traps and guns make it easier to hunt large numbers of animals, causing:

- A significant decrease in the number of the hunted species.
- Disruption of food chains.

Wild meat – taken from the natural environment (not agricultural) threatens biodiversity because:

- Hunting is unsustainable.
- More animals can be killed than are produced naturally.

Conserving biodiversity through controlling hunting:

- There is a total ban on hunting for wild meat in many countries.
- Park rangers patrol nature reserves.
- Educational programmes are being introduced to explain the harms of large-scale hunting.

3. Fishing

Overfishing is a threat because:

- Removing large amounts of one species means the population is not given a chance to recover its numbers.
- Nets with small mesh sizes catch young fish, which are not used for food and usually dumped.
- Some nets drag along the seabed, catching everything in their path.

Conserving biodiversity within fishing:

- Fish quotas are used by the EU to safeguard fish numbers.
- Each country is allowed to catch a fixed amount of certain fish species per year.

4. Agriculture

Monoculture – agricultural practice where only one species is produced.

It allows us to produce a large amount of food at a lower cost.

Monoculture threatens biodiversity because:

- Other plants are prevented from growing.
- Animals that relied on those plants for food/shelter can no longer live.

Overuse of herbicides/pesticides – these kill organisms that damage crops, reducing competition between crops and plants and crops and insects.

- Reduces the variety of species found in an area.
- They can stay in the environment for a long time.
- Can be passed to other organisms through the food chain.

Overuse of fertilisers – substances that are added to supply nutrients to soil.

- Can be natural or artificial.
- Absorbed by plants through the soil.
- Increases the growth of plants and therefore the amount of food which can be produced.

Overuse of fertilisers is a threat to the freshwater diversity because:

- Fertilisers can seep into streams, rivers and lakes.
- This causes algae to grow in the water, which can block light that is needed for water plants to photosynthesise.
- When the algae dies it decomposes, using up large amounts of oxygen in the water.

Solutions for the threat posed by modern agricultural practices:

- Provide economic incentives for conserving biodiversity.
  - GLAS scheme: provides funding to farmers in return for environmental management on their land.
- Organic farming – it does not use chemical herbicides/pesticides.
- Crop rotation – when different species of crops are grown in a field each year.
- Offer support and certification to farmers who practise sustainable food production.
  - **Example:** The Rainforest Alliance.

Humans can reverse other forms of environmental damage by making the right choices. For example, reducing use of CFCs will allow the ozone to rebuild and protect the planet from excess UV rays.

Sample Questions

Section A

1. Outline some of the ways in which we depend on other species of plants and animals for our survival.

   Food/antibiotics/produce goods.

2. List two ways in which humans threaten biodiversity.

   Hunting/overfishing.

3. Pick one aspect of food production that threatens biodiversity and outline the measures that are being taken to reduce its impact on biodiversity.

   Overuse of herbicides in agriculture can cause runoff into streams or affect non-target plants, reducing the number of species in an area. Farmers may introduce natural predators to control pests instead of artificial ones.

Section B

1. Why do you think biodiversity is important?

   Each organism has a role to play and more biodiversity in an ecosystem means increased productivity. For humans, this could influence food, medicine and agriculture.

2. How does slurry affect the biodiversity in rivers and lakes?

   Slurry can run off and pollute rivers and lakes. It can cause an algal bloom, which eventually runs out of food and dies. This starves the other plants and animals in the environment.

3. Why do you think the EU introduces fish quotas every year? What type of data is analysed and collected before these quotas are decided?

   Fish quotas make sure that fish numbers stay healthy enough to allow for reproduction and sustainable fishing.

   Scientists would study estimated numbers mating, breeding and travel patterns of the fish as well as demand from consumers.

14 Studying Habitats and Their Communities

 Learning Outcomes

5. Conduct a habitat study; research and investigate the adaptation, competition and interdependence of organisms within specific habitats and communities.

8. Explain how matter and energy flow through ecosystems.

aims By the end of this chapter you should:
- conduct a habitat study and produce relevant data
- be able to describe the flow of matter and energy through living things
- illustrate and discuss a relevant food chain to your studied habitat
- be able to discuss relationships within an ecosystem

Habitat – the place where an animal or plant lives.

Community – a group of animals and plants that live together.

Ecosystem – a group of plants and animals and their environment.

key point

ECOLOGY
The study of ecosystems.

Habitat Study

Step 1 – Mapping an ecosystem
- Map out the ecosystem.
- Include a **legend** to explain key points of the map.

Step 2 – Measuring environmental factors
- **Abiotic factors** – non-living, e.g. air temperature.
- **Biotic factors** – living, e.g. flora.

Abiotic Factor	Measuring Equipment
Air, water and soil temperature	Thermometer/soil thermometer
Light intensity	Light meter
Aspect	Compass
Wind speed	Anemometer

Step 3 – Observing and identifying animals present in the habitat (biotic factors)

- Large animals can be observed from a distance.
- Smaller animals need to be collected to be identified.

Sweep Net	Pooter	Pitfall Trap
Use: capture small bugs from bushes	Use: collect small bugs by sucking them up	Use: collect small insects as they walk along the ground

Step 4 – Identifying unknown species

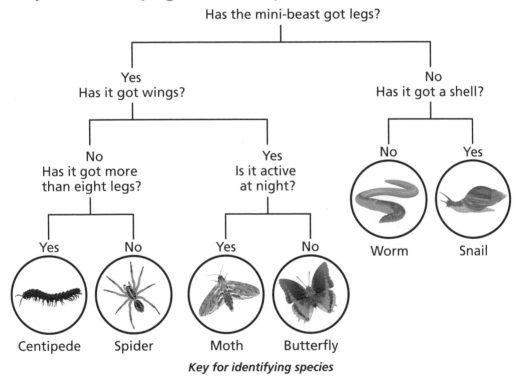

Key for identifying species

- Use a book with a key to identify any unknown species.
- **Key** – a system for identifying organisms based on answering questions about the physical features of an organism.

Step 5 – Observing and identifying plants present in a habitat

Quadrat

Use: Square frame used to estimate the number of plants in a habitat. Place your quadrat at random by throwing over your shoulder or simply placing it in any location. Count the number of particular plants present and record findings.

Using a quadrat

Percentage frequency

- Quantitative data.
- Estimates how often a particular type of plant turns up in an area.

The Flow of Matter and Energy through Ecosystems

1. The flow of matter

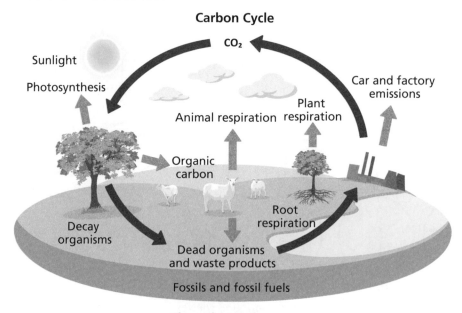

The carbon cycle

2. The flow of energy

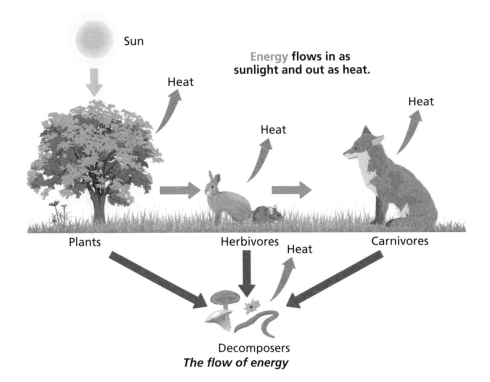

Energy **flows in as sunlight and out as heat.**

Sun

Heat

Heat

Heat

Plants

Herbivores

Heat

Carnivores

Decomposers
The flow of energy

Food Chains

- **Carnivore** – eats meat only.
- **Herbivore** – eats plants only.
- **Omnivore** – eats meat and plants.
- **Food webs** – series of interconnecting food chains.
- **Producer** – makes own food.
- **Consumer** – eats other organisms.
- **Decomposer** – recycles dead organic matter.

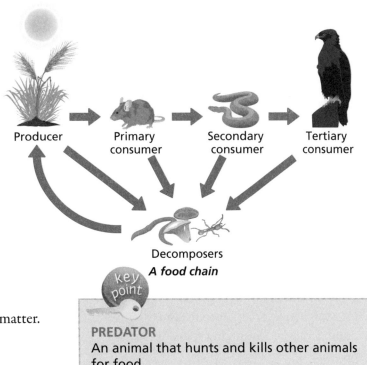

Producer

Primary consumer

Secondary consumer

Tertiary consumer

Decomposers
A food chain

key point

PREDATOR
An animal that hunts and kills other animals for food.

PREY
An animal that is hunted and killed for food.

FOOD CHAINS

A sequence of organisms where each one is eaten by the next. Each time an organism is consumed the matter and energy it contains is passed on to the organism that consumed it.

Energy transfer in a food chain

- At each stage of a food chain only 10% of available energy is passed on to the next organism.
- The other 90% is used by the plant/animal for movement, respiration, or is released into the environment as heat or waste.

Relationships within an Ecosystem

1. Investigating adaptation

To investigate you will need to consider:

- The physical features you observe.
- Patterns of growth or behaviour you observe.
- What you think the organism needs to survive in this environment.
- Research that other scientists have carried out on this species.
  — **Example:** Hares growing a winter coat to stay warm.

2. Investigating competition

Competition is the struggle between organisms for limited resources.

To investigate you will need to consider:

- What resources seem to be in limited supply.
- Which organisms are competing with each other.
- The adaptation that allows organisms to compete successfully.
- Research that other scientists have investigated.
  — **Example:** In a habitat a number of animals seek to find space, food, water and partners.

Line transect

Use: A piece of twine marked at regular intervals across a habitat to measure numbers and variation in types of plants present.

A line transect

3. Investigating interdependence

To investigate you will need to consider:

- Which organisms appear to interact with each other.
- How each organism appears to benefit from the relationship.
- How each organism appears to be adapted to benefit from the other.
- Research that other scientists have carried out.
  - **Example:** Many insects are pollinators. They transfer pollen from one flower to another so that plants can reproduce. In turn, insects get food as a reward for their work.

INTERDEPENDENCE is the way that plants and animals rely on each other.

Sample Paper 2019

Question 14

A group of students carried out a habitat study.

(a) Use some of the words in the list to name the pieces of equipment shown below, which can be used in a habitat study.

Beating tray   **Pooter**   **Net**   **Pitfall trap**

Picture	Name
	Pitfall trap
	Pooter

(b) The students also used a quadrat during their habitat study.

(i) What shape is a quadrat? Describe how the students might have used the quadrat.

Square. Thrown it randomly a number of times in their habitat and recorded plant species they encountered in the quadrat each time.

(ii) In one part of the habitat, the students used the quadrat 30 times and found that a certain species was present on 18 occasions. Calculate the percentage frequency of that species.

$\frac{18}{30} = .6 = 60\%.$

Sample Questions

Section A

1. Draw a simple diagram to represent a food chain. List what type of organism is found at each stage of the food chain (e.g. producer).

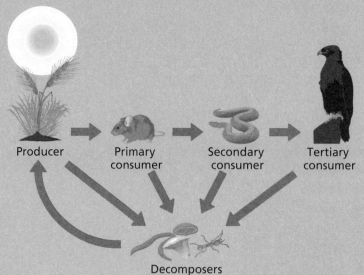

| Producer | Primary consumer | Secondary consumer | Tertiary consumer |

Decomposers

2. Explain how ecosystems benefit from decomposers.

Decomposers break down dead plants and animals and any waste in an ecosystem, recycling nutrients back into the soil for plants to use.

3. Name the piece of apparatus that could be used for:

(a) Measuring soil temperature.
Thermometer.

(b) Measuring wind speed.
Anemometer.

(c) Collecting small insects.
Pooter.

4. Explain why there are normally only small animals at the bottom of a food chain, and larger animals at the top of a food chain. Explain how energy is transferred between these organisms.

    Within the food chain energy can be passed and transferred from one organism to another. Plants produce energy from the Sun during photosynthesis. They are then consumed by other organisms, transferring energy. Usually small animals are consumed by bigger ones as they go up the food chain.

Section B

1. What is competition? Give two examples of competition that you can observe in your local park.

    Competition is the struggle between two organisms for the same resource in an environment.

    Plants competing for light. Birds competing for insects.

2. What is interdependence? Give an example of interdependence that you can observe in your local park.

    All organisms in an ecosystem depend on each other for survival. This is interdependence. For example, a plant provides food for an animal which in turn spreads its seed when it egests food.

Earth and Space

Contents

Climate Change

➡ **Learning Outcome**

7. Illustrate how Earth's processes and human factors influence Earth's climate, evaluate effects of climate change and outline initiatives that attempt to address those effects.

aims By the end of this chapter you should:
  - be able to define key terms associated with climate and climate change
  - understand the natural greenhouse effect
  - be able to discuss ocean currents and their effect on climate
  - examine the causes and effects of climate change

Climate

Weather – the atmospheric conditions in a particular area at a particular time.

  - Weather conditions can change by the hour.

Climate – describes weather conditions in a large area over a long period of time.

Atmosphere – layer of gases that surround the Earth.

  - Protects the Earth from the Sun's harmful radiation.
  - Keeps the planet warm enough for life to exist.

Greenhouse gases – gases including carbon dioxide, methane, water vapour and nitrous oxide.

  - Trap heat energy that is radiated out from the Earth towards space.

key point

CLIMATE CHANGE

When there is a change in the weather conditions in an area over a long period of time.

exam focus

THE NATURAL GREENHOUSE EFFECT

1. The Sun sends out heat and light energy.
2. The Earth's atmosphere reflects some of this energy back into space.
3. The land and seas absorb the rest of this energy.
4. This energy is then radiated back towards space.
5. The greenhouse gases then trap some of this energy.
6. This helps to even out temperatures on Earth, and supports life.

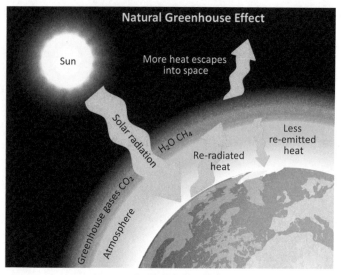

Natural greenhouse effect

The Ozone Layer

The ozone layer is the part of the atmosphere that protects Earth by absorbing most of the Sun's harmful radiation.

- Contains ozone (O_3).

Chlorofluorocarbons (CFCs) are man-made chemicals.

- Contain carbon, chlorine and fluorine.
- Were used in fridges, aerosol cans and the production of plastics.
- Damage the ozone layer, allowing more of the Sun's energy to reach the Earth. This contributes to global warming.

Wind and Ocean Currents

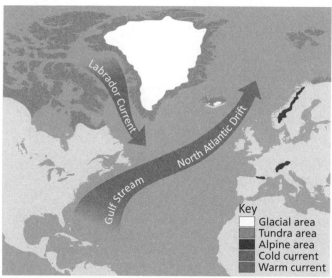

Ocean currents that affect climate

- Warm air rises at the equator and drifts to the poles, while cooler air falls and moves in the opposite direction.
- Cold water from the North Atlantic sinks and moves down towards the equator, while warm water moves up from the Gulf of Mexico.
- This gives Ireland its mild climate.

Climate Change

Climate changes due to natural processes:

1. **Ice age** – a period of cold temperature in which ice sheets cover large parts of the Earth.
   - There have been at least five major ice ages so far.
   - Caused by slight changes in the Earth's orbit around the Sun.
   - Results in a change in the amount of solar energy our planet receives.

2. **Volcanic activity** – eruptions lead to large amounts of dust and sulphur dioxide gas being released into the atmosphere.
   - Causes temporary cooling.

Climate change due to human activities:

Sources of greenhouse gases from human activity

Greenhouse Gas	Sources
Carbon Dioxide (CO_2) Main gas responsible for global warming	- Burning fossil fuels - Respiration - Decay and burning wood - Cement production
Methane (CH_4) Traps 21 times more heat than the same amount of CO_2, but there is much less of this in the atmosphere	- Coal mining - Landfill sites - Natural gas leaks - Rice paddies - Waste gas from livestock
Nitrous Oxide (N_2O) Can trap 270 times more heat than CO_2	- Burning fossil fuels - Fertilisers

Fossil fuels – substances such as coal, oil and natural gas formed over millions of years from the remains of plants and animals.

- First used to operate machinery during the Industrial Revolution in the 18th and 19th centuries.

key point

GLOBAL WARMING

The accelerated increase in the temperature of the Earth due to rising levels of greenhouse gases in the atmosphere.

- Burning fossil fuels, intensive farming, and cutting down and burning rainforests lead to the release of greenhouse gases and the acceleration of climate change.

Effects of climate change

1. Droughts and heat waves
This can lead to:
- Heat stroke
- Fires

2. More violent storms
Warmer waters cause heat energy to transfer to the air above, resulting in more evaporation of water.
This can lead to:
- Flooding
- Destruction of habitat for both humans and animals

3. Rising sea levels
This can lead to:
- Erosion
- Flooding

4. Warming oceans
This can lead to:
- Coral bleaching
- Loss of breeding ground

5. Ocean acidification
Carbonic acid is formed when CO_2 is mixed with water, making the oceans more acidic.
This can lead to:
- Dissolved shells
- Less food/disrupted food chain

6. Melting of the polar ice caps
This can lead to:
- Rising sea levels
- Weather/climate changes

How climate change may affect Ireland

- More rain, more flooding.
- Frequent storms.
- Warmer, drier summers.
- Dried grasses replacing the green countryside.
- Higher temperatures and lower rainfall in summer may negatively affect our freshwater supplies.
- Farmers may no longer be able to grow potatoes.
- Bog bursts may be more frequent.

Evidence of a changing atmosphere

Ice core data
These are cylinders of ice drilled out of an ice sheet or glacier.

- They contain small bubbles of air which are samples of the atmosphere from when they were trapped.
- Carbon dating allows scientists to date these bubbles.

Initiatives to Address Climate Change

The United Nations Framework Convention on Climate Change (UNFCCC) – an international treaty where member countries joined together to consider what they could do to limit global warming.

- Encourages countries to stabilise greenhouse gas concentrations.
- It does not set compulsory limits.

The Kyoto Protocol – an international agreement to reduce greenhouse gas emissions.

- Each country has a target for limiting/reducing carbon emissions.
- These are mandatory limits in which each country has a certain number of units of carbon they can release.
- If they do not reach these quotas, they can sell their units to other countries or store them for the future.

The Paris Agreement – the UN climate change conference took place in Paris in 2015 and negotiated the following agreements:

- Aim to limit global warming to less than two degrees above pre-industrial level.
- Stop burning fossil fuels by 2100.
- Aim to have zero net carbon emissions by 2100.
- Meet every five years to discuss progress and set new targets.
- Rich nations will help poorer ones with the cost of reducing carbon emissions.

What Can We Do?

We as individuals can reduce our carbon footprint, i.e. the amount of greenhouse gases released into the atmosphere as a result of our activities. Ways of doing so include:

- Walking or cycling instead of driving when possible.
- Opting for public transport over driving cars.
- Reducing the number of flights that we take.
- Using energy-saving light bulbs.
- Spending less time in the shower.
- Turning electrical equipment off after use.
- Turning the heating down by 1 °C.
- Insulating our homes.

Sample Questions

Section A

1. How do ocean currents affect the climate in Ireland?

   Warm water moves up from the Gulf of Mexico, giving Ireland a mild climate.

2. List the human activities that release greenhouse gases into the atmosphere.

   – Burning fossil fuels.
   – Respiration.
   – Decay and burning wood.
   – Cement production.

3. Global warming causes the oceans to become warmer. What are the effects of warmer oceans?

   Warmer oceans can lead to coral bleaching, loss of breeding ground for animals and change in climate.

4. What would life be like on Earth if the atmosphere did not contain greenhouse gases?

   The Earth's temperature would be significantly lower without the gases trapping heat from the Sun. (Average temperature approximately –18 °C)

Section B

1. Is weather and climate the same thing? Explain your answer.

   No; weather refers to the atmospheric conditions in a particular area at a particular time (weather conditions can change quickly).

   Climate describes weather conditions in a large area over a long period of time.

2. What changes occurred in the atmosphere as a result of the Industrial Revolution? Explain your answer.

   The use of chemicals and fuel in factories resulted in increased air and water pollution and an increased use of fossil fuels. The world also saw huge population growth, leading to a bigger demand for resources and widespread pollution.

3. Which aspect of global warming would affect polar bears? Explain your answer.

   The melting of sea ice would destroy their hunting grounds, as they use sea ice as a platform to catch seals.

4. Which aspect of climate change would have the biggest effect on the people in your community? Explain your answer.

   More frequent violent storms can cause major disruption and potential accidents.

5. List ways in which you as an individual can reduce your carbon footprint, and how your community as a whole can do the same.

   – Reduce, reuse, recycle.
   – Drive less.
   – Switch to sustainable clean energy.

16 Energy Sources

6. Research different energy sources; formulate and communicate an informed view of ways that current and future energy needs on Earth can be met.

aims By the end of this chapter you should:
- reflect on the use of different energy sources
- be able to describe the process by which fossil fuels are made
- recognise types of renewable energy sources and outline their benefits

Non-renewable Energy Sources

Non-renewable energy sources take a long time to form and cannot be replaced when they have been used up.

Coal

It took millions of years for coal to form from land plants, huge ancient fern forests that existed over 300 million years ago.

Oil and Gas

It took at least a million years for oil and gas to form from ocean plants, like phytoplankton and algae, hundreds of millions of years ago.

Huge forests grew 300 million years ago covering most of the land.

The vegetation dies and forms peat.

Peat is compressed to form lignite.

Further compression forms bituminous coal.

Eventually anthracite forms.

Heat

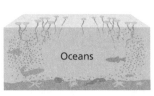

Oceans

Marine plants and animals die and sink to the bottom of the seabed.

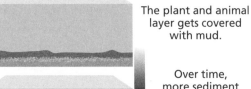

The plant and animal layer gets covered with mud.

Over time, more sediment creates pressure, compressing the dead plants and animals into oil.

Pressure

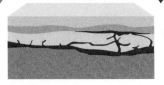

Oil moves up through porous rocks and eventually forms a reservoir.

Formation of fossil fuels

Fossil fuels

Coal, oil, natural gas.

Advantages:

- Easy to find.
- Easy to transport.
- Create jobs in the industry.

Disadvantages:

- Cause environmental degradation.
- Lead to poor air quality, which harms human health.
- Finite resource, i.e. they will eventually run out.

Nuclear energy

Produced by splitting uranium atoms in a nuclear reactor to release huge amounts of heat energy. This is called nuclear fission.

Advantages:

- No greenhouse gas emissions.
- Produces cheap electricity.

Disadvantages:

- Can be dangerous due to accidental release of harmful radioactive materials.
- Safe radioactive waste disposal is very difficult and expensive.
- High cost of nuclear plant construction.

Renewable Energy Sources

Renewable energy is energy derived from Earth's natural resources that are not finite.

1. Wind energy

Currently there are 228 wind farms in Ireland. These farms have generated up to 20% of our electricity in recent years. A wind turbine converts the motion energy of wind into electrical energy.

Advantages:

- Non-finite.
- No greenhouse gas emissions.
- No fuel costs.

Disadvantages:

- Requires wind to work.
- Manufacture and implementation can be costly.

Wind turbines

2. Solar energy

Energy from sunlight can cause some chemicals to release electrons. Photovoltaic cells in solar panels use this property to produce electricity. These cells produce an electric current when light and heat strike them.

Advantages:

- Non-finite.
- No greenhouse gas emissions.
- No fuel costs.

Disadvantages:

- Solar cells don't work at night.
- Solar cells can be expensive.

Solar panels

3. Geothermal energy

Uses the heat contained under the Earth's surface to generate electricity. Water is pumped through pipes in the ground where it is warmed and then returned to the surface.

Advantages:

- Non-finite.
- No fuel costs.
- Minimal environmental impact.

Disadvantages:

- High up-front costs.
- Can cause earthquakes.

4. Hydroelectric energy

The motion of moving water is used to generate electricity. Water is held behind a dam and when it is released, it powers generators within the dam.

Advantages:

- Non-finite.
- No fuel costs.
- No greenhouse gas emission.

Disadvantages:

- Environmental damage.
- Expensive to construct.

Energy Needs in Ireland

The amount of energy used in Ireland for:

- Electricity = 20%
- Heating = 40%
- Transport = 40%

key point

Most of our energy comes from non-renewable fossil fuels.

Ireland has set a target to reduce the amount of fossil fuels we burn. The Government has pledged to generate 70% of the country's electricity supply from renewable sources by 2030.

Global Energy Needs

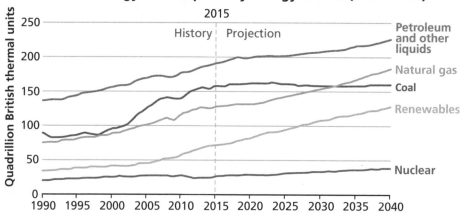

World energy consumption by energy source (1990–2040)

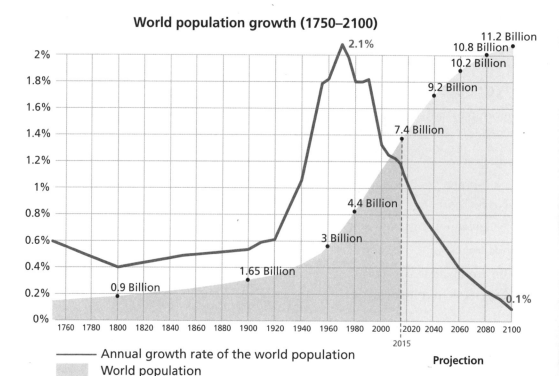

World population growth (1750–2100)

Sample Questions

(Use the graphs on the previous page for help)

Section A

1. Why do you think the demand for energy has increased since the 1980s?

   Advances in technology have caused energy demands to increase, e.g. the increase in airline traffic.

2. What source of energy is used to meet most of the world's needs? What are the advantages and disadvantages of using this source of energy?

   Oil and gas (fossil fuels) account for most of the world's energy.

   An advantage is that they are relatively safe when compared to nuclear energy. However, a disadvantage is that they cause pollution and are finite.

3. What is the leading source of renewable energy in the world? What are the advantages of using this type of renewable energy compared to continuing to use fossil fuels?

   Hydropower is the most widely used renewable power source. It is a clean fuel source unlike fossil fuels.

Section B

1. Draw two diagrams explaining how both coal/peat, and oil/gas are formed.

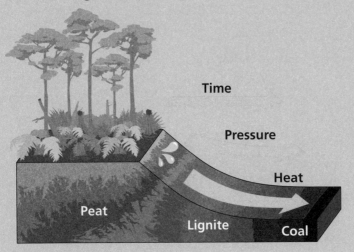

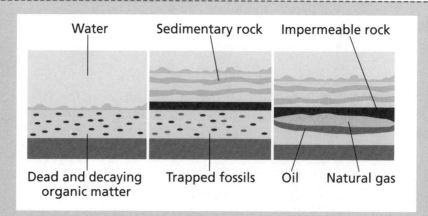

2. Solar and wind energy are described as being intermittent energy sources. What does this mean and why is this a problem?

   This means it is not continuously available for conversion into electricity as the original energy, e.g. wind, is outside direct control. This may cause problems with demand.

3. Suggest how Ireland may meet its goal of reducing the amount of fossil fuels we burn.

   Promote the use of vehicles that produce less pollution.

   Promote the use of energy efficient or cleaner non-fossil fuel homes. Increase carbon and fossil fuel tax.

Learning Outcome

5. Describe the cycling of matter, including that of carbon and water, linking it with biological and atmospheric phenomena.

By the end of this chapter you should:
- be able to describe the cycling of matter, including that of carbon and water
- be able to discuss the changing levels of carbon dioxide
- know how to explain chemical reactions involving carbon dioxide

The Water Cycle

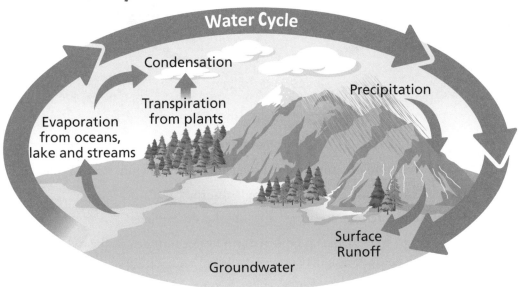

Water Cycle

Condensation

Precipitation

Transpiration from plants

Evaporation from oceans, lake and streams

Surface Runoff

Groundwater

The water cycle

1. **Evaporation** – heat from the Sun causes water to evaporate from the oceans and other bodies of water. Water also transpires from leaves and plants and adds to the evaporation.

2. **Condensation** – water vapour is cooled and condenses into tiny droplets that form clouds.

exam focus

Know how to explain the cycle and processes, as many exam questions can stem from this.

3. **Precipitation** – as clouds cool further, the tiny droplets merge to form bigger droplets, which fall as rain, sleet, or snow.

4. **Collection** – this water collects in rivers and streams or seeps underground.

The Carbon Cycle

Living things contain organic compounds, which contain carbon. Carbon is constantly moved from living organisms into the environment and back again, so it never runs out.

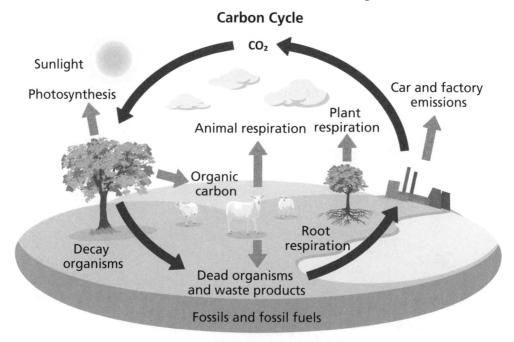

The carbon cycle

1. CO_2 is removed from the atmosphere during photosynthesis and stored by plants.

2. Plants are eaten by animals and the carbon is absorbed also.

3. Plants and animals respire, releasing CO_2 into the atmosphere.

4. Animals produce waste, which is broken down by decomposers in the soil. This releases CO_2 into the atmosphere.

5. Plants and animals are also broken down by decomposers when they die, which releases CO_2 into the atmosphere.

6. These dead plants and animals may also form fossil fuels, over million of years, if they are not broken down. Burning fossil fuels releases CO_2.

7. Oceans absorb and store CO_2. Movements of the ocean releases CO_2 back into the atmosphere.

Changing levels of carbon dioxide

- **Seasonal levels of CO_2 in the atmosphere**
  - Level of CO_2 in the atmosphere changes at different times in the year.
  - More photosynthesis occurs during the summer, meaning CO_2 levels are lower.
  - In autumn and winter the leaves fall off the trees, reducing the amount of photosynthesis occurring.
- **Carbon sinks**
  - Reservoirs that store large amounts of carbon compounds (e.g oceans and forests).
  - They absorb around one third of CO_2 in the atmosphere.

The global carbon budget – describes the amount of CO_2 being released into the atmosphere compared with how much is being removed.

- A balanced carbon budget describes a situation in which the rate of CO_2 being released is approximately the same as that being removed.

Chemical reactions involving carbon dioxide

key point

PHOTOSYNTHESIS
A chemical reaction that occurs in plants in which light energy from the Sun is converted to chemical energy within the plant.

Photosynthesis

$$6CO_2 \quad + \quad 6H_2O \quad \xrightarrow[\text{Sunlight}]{\text{Chlorophyll}} \quad C_6H_{12}O_6 \quad + \quad 6O_2$$

$$\text{Carbon Dioxide} + \text{Water} \quad \xrightarrow[\text{Chlorophyll}]{\text{Sunlight}} \quad \text{Glucose} + \text{Oxygen}$$

Respiration

$$C_6H_{12}O_6 \quad + \quad 6O_2 \quad \longrightarrow \quad 6CO_2 \quad + \quad 6H_2O \quad + \quad \text{ATP}$$

$$\text{Glucose} + \text{Oxygen} \quad \longrightarrow \quad \text{Carbon Dioxide} + \text{Water} + \text{Energy}$$

RESPIRATION

A chemical reaction that occurs in the cells of living organisms; energy is released from glucose and produces carbon dioxide and water.

Combustion – burning of wood/fossil fuels, which releases heat energy from the fuel. Carbon dioxide and water vapour are produced.

Combustion

$$CH_4 \quad + \quad 2O_2 \quad \longrightarrow \quad CO_2 \quad + \quad 2H_2O$$

Methane + Oxygen ⟶ Carbon Dioxide + Water

Decomposition – living organisms break down dead organic matter or waste, releasing nutrients contained within the organic matter into the environment.

Exam Paper 2019

Question 3

The diagram below illustrates the water cycle.
Some of the key stages of the water cycle are labelled **1, 2, 3** and **4**.

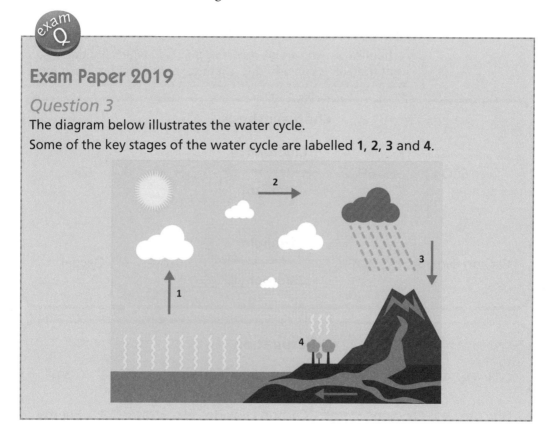

(a) Complete the table below using the numbers **1, 2, 3** or **4** to match each of the labelled processes shown in the diagram with the correct description.

Process	1, 2, 3 or 4?
Air currents cause clouds to move onshore	2
Water falls to the Earth as precipitation	3
Heat from the Sun converts liquid water into water vapour	1
Plants lose water through the process of transpiration	4

(3 × 4)

(b) In 2018 Ireland experienced low rainfall throughout the year. This led to water shortages and restrictions on water use.

Describe one way in which water usage in a home could be reduced.
By turning off taps when you are not using them, e.g. when you are brushing your teeth/drying your hands. (3)

Sample Paper 2019

Question 5

The diagram below shows some of the processes involved in the carbon cycle.

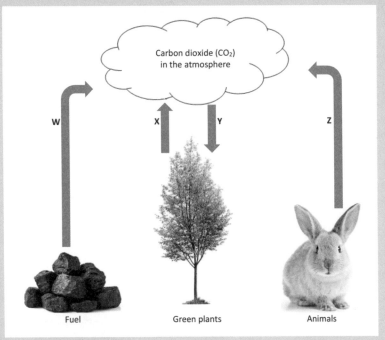

Carbon dioxide (CO₂) in the atmosphere

W   X   Y   Z

Fuel   Green plants   Animals

Each of the blue arrows **W, X, Y** and **Z** represents one of the following three processes:

Respiration   Photosynthesis   Combustion

In the table below, write the name of each process.
(Note that one process appears twice.)

Process	Name
W	Combustion
X	Respiration
Y	Photosynthesis
Z	Respiration

Sample Questions

Section A

1. Explain how a puddle of water that you may see in the morning on your way to school can disappear by the evening time when you are on your way home.

   Evaporation causes the water to change into a gaseous state and be absorbed into the atmosphere as water vapour.

2. Would you say the amount of water on Earth increases, decreases, or stays the same? Explain your answer.

   The amount of water on Earth stays the same. However, what can change is the state that water is in.

3. Why is there a seasonal variation in the amount of CO_2 in the atmosphere?

   The variation coincides with plants' uptake of carbon dioxide for photosynthesis.

4. Explain how cutting down forests leads to an increase in CO_2 levels in the atmosphere.

   With deforestation, trees are not absorbing carbon dioxide as fast as it is being produced, leading to increased levels.

Section B

1. (a) What role do oceans play in the carbon cycle?

   Oceans absorb and store carbon dioxide.

   (b) Describe the roles that animals play in the carbon cycle.

   Animals feed on plants, passing the carbon compounds along the food chain. Animals exhale most of this carbon as carbon dioxide. When animals die, decomposers break down their bodies, returning carbon to the atmosphere.

2. Describe one process that releases CO_2 into the atmosphere, and one that removes CO_2 from the atmosphere.

Respiration releases CO_2 into the atmosphere as it is a waste product of energy production.

Photosynthesis removes CO_2 from the atmosphere and turns it into glucose.

3. How would using renewable energy sources like wind and solar energy, instead of burning fossil fuels, affect the global carbon budget? How would planting more trees affect the global carbon budget?

Using renewable energy sources would lower the amount of carbon being produced and let into the atmosphere.

Planting more trees would mean more carbon dioxide is being absorbed from the atmosphere.

18 The Earth, Sun and Moon

⇨ **Learning Outcomes**

1. Describe the relationships between various celestial objects including moons, asteroids, comets, planets, stars, solar systems, galaxies and space.

4. Develop and use a model of the Earth-Sun-Moon system to describe predictable phenomena observable on Earth, including seasons, lunar phases, and eclipses of the Sun and the Moon.

 By the end of this chapter you should:
- consider what causes day and night, the seasons and the lunar cycle
- be able to discuss the different types of eclipse

The Earth, Sun and Moon

The Sun – the star at the centre of our solar system.

The Earth – one of the eight planets in our solar system.

The Moon – a natural satellite of the Earth.

The Earth-Sun-Moon System – the interactions between the Earth, the Sun and the Moon.

Day and Night

Earth rotates on its axis.

- One rotation = 24 hours.
- Only half the Earth faces the Sun at any one time in a rotation.
- The amount of daylight a place experiences during a 24-hour rotation depends on its latitude and the time of year.

Latitude – a measure of how far north or south a place is in relation to the equator.

- Measured in degrees.
- Latitude at the equator = $0°$.
- Latitude at the North and South poles = $90°$.

The Seasons

Understanding the seasons is key to understanding conditions on Earth.

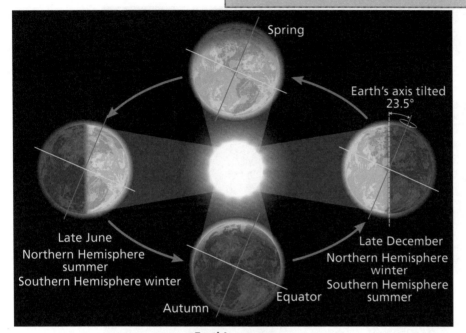

Earth's seasons

The Earth has seasons because its axis is tilted.

- The Earth rotates on its axis as it orbits the Sun, but the axis always points in the same direction.
- During the summer months in the Northern Hemisphere, the Earth is tilted towards the Sun, receiving the Sun's most direct rays. During the winter, it is tilted away from the Sun.
- Throughout the year, different parts of Earth receive the Sun's most direct rays. When the North Pole tilts towards the Sun, it's summer in the Northern Hemisphere. When the South Pole tilts towards the Sun, it is winter in the Northern Hemisphere.
- The day that the North Pole is tilted closest to the Sun is known as the summer solstice. The winter solstice occurs when the North Pole is tilted farthest from the Sun.

The Earth's axis is tilted

The Phases of the Moon

As the Moon rotates around the Earth, the portion of illuminated Moon you are able to see changes, resulting in **the phases of the Moon**.

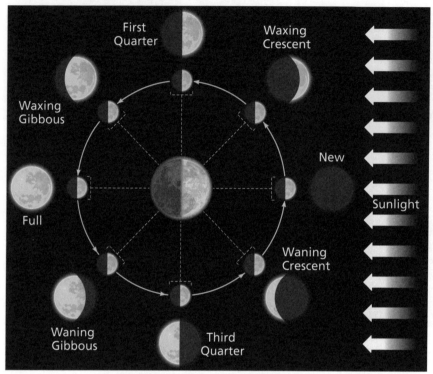

The phases of the Moon

Lunar cycle – a period of approximately 29.5 days during which the Moon completes a full orbit of Earth and appears in all of the lunar phases.

Waxing Moon – when the illuminated area of the Moon is increasing.

Waning Moon – when the illuminated area of the Moon is decreasing.

The Moon does not generate its own light.

- Light from the Sun is reflected off the Moon.
- The Sun illuminates the Moon.

Tides

The tides – the rising and falling of water in the oceans caused by the gravity and position of the Sun and the Moon in relation to the Earth.

- The tides rise and fall twice each day.
- High tide = when the sea is at its highest level.
- Low tide = when the sea is at its lowest level.

Spring tides – when the Earth, Sun and Moon are all aligned (at New Moon and Full Moon).

- High tides are higher than normal and low tides are lower than normal.

Neap tides – when the Sun and Moon are at right angles to the Earth (at the first and third quarter of the Moon).

- Only a small difference in high and low tides.

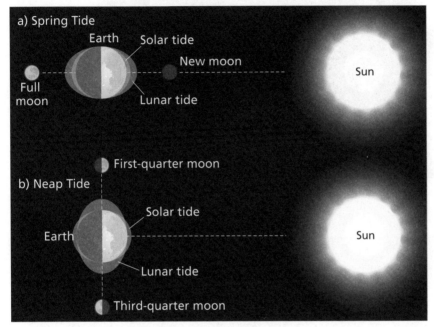

Spring tide and neap tide

Solar Eclipse

Occurs when the Moon is positioned directly between the Earth and the Sun, blocking out the light from the Sun.

- The shadow of the Moon then falls on the Earth.
- The centre of the shadow is completely dark and is called the **umbra**.
- The area outside the centre is less dark and is called the **penumbra**.

Total solar eclipse – people who are in the umbra during the solar eclipse see the Moon completely blocking out the Sun.

Partial solar eclipse – people in the penumbra see the Moon blocking out only part of the Sun.

Lunar Eclipse

Occurs when the Earth is directly between the Sun and the Moon, casting a shadow on the surface of the Moon.

Results in sections of the Moon that are normally illuminated appearing dark.

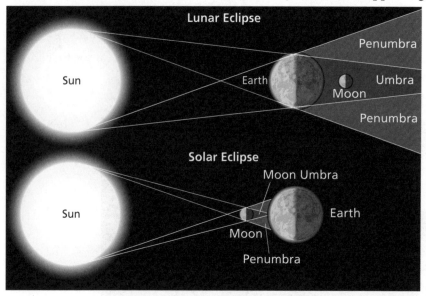

Lunar eclipse and solar eclipse

Exam Paper 2019

Question 16

2019 marks the 50th anniversary of man's first landing on the Moon. Since then there have been a number of other missions to the Moon.

(a) The diagram below shows the Earth orbiting the Sun.

Complete the diagram to show the shape, location and motion of the Moon in the Earth–Sun–Moon system.

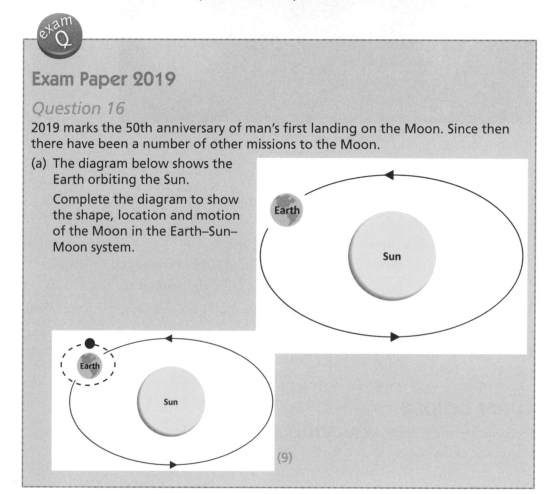

(9)

(b) At the time of the first landing, the Moon was in a waxing crescent phase as seen from Earth.

   (i) The images below show different phases of the Moon in sequence, from left to right. Place a tick (✔) in the box beneath the image which shows the Moon in a waxing crescent phase.

      ✔   ☐   ☐   ☐ (3)

   (ii) Shade in the image of the Moon below to illustrate the next phase of the Moon in the sequence above.

(3)

(c) On January 2nd 2019, the Chinese Chang'e–4 lander touched down on the far side or 'dark side' of the Moon.

Explain why this side of the Moon is never visible from Earth.
The Moon spins on its axis (3)
at same rate (in the same time) it takes to orbit the Earth. (3)

Sample Questions

Section A

1. What causes the phases of the Moon?

   They are determined by the angle from which we observe it from Earth. The Moon reflects the Sun's light and we see different fractions of it illuminated as it orbits the Earth.

2. Describe what you would see during a total eclipse of the Sun if you were looking down at the Earth from the Moon?

   Darkness, as the Moon is blocking the Sun's light.

3. Explain the difference between a total solar eclipse and a partial solar eclipse.

   Total solar eclipse – the Moon covers the Sun completely.

   Partial solar eclipse – the Moon slightly covers the Sun.

4. The same side of the Moon is always visible from Earth even though the Moon rotates on its own axis. Explain how this can be the case.

   The Moon rotates on its axis at the same rate that it orbits Earth, meaning we only see one side.

5. Can you see a New Moon? Explain your answer.

   No, because a New Moon is not in the sky at night. The closest you can see is a Waxing Crescent.

6. At which phase of the Moon is a solar eclipse possible?

   New Moon.

Section B

1. Draw a diagram of the Earth, the Moon, and the Sun. Indicate the position of the Moon during the following lunar phases: a) New Moon b) First Quarter c) Full Moon d) Third Quarter.

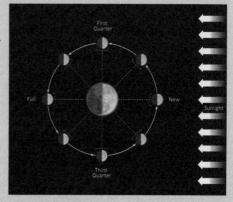

2. Explain why the Northern and Southern hemispheres experience different seasons at the same time of year.

   The tilt of the Earth means that different hemispheres are leaning towards or away from the Sun at different times of the year. This change in distance, and thus temperature, causes the seasons.

 Earth and Other Planets

 Learning Outcome

3. Interpret data to compare the Earth with other planets and moons in the solar system, with respect to properties including mass, gravity, size, and composition.

aims By the end of this chapter you should:
- examine Earth relative to other celestial bodies
- be able to calculate force and mass

Earth and Other Planets

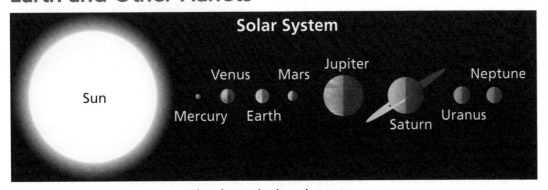

The planets in the solar system

Planets in relation to their distance from the Sun:

Mercury, Venus, Earth, Mars, Jupiter, Saturn, Uranus, Neptune

(My Very Enthusiastic Mother Just Served Us Noodles)

Comparing Mass

Relative mass – the mass of one object compared with another.

Example: Relative mass of Mars compared with Earth.

 key point

Size does not equal mass.
This is why Earth can have a higher mass than Jupiter but be much smaller in size.

$$\frac{\text{Mass of Mars}}{\text{Mass of Earth}} \quad = \quad \frac{6.42 \times 10^{23} \text{ kg}}{5.97 \times 10^{24} \text{ kg}} \quad = \quad \frac{1}{9} \quad = \quad 0.11$$

Comparing Size

$$\text{Relative Radius of a Space Object} \quad = \quad \frac{\text{Radius of a Space Object}}{\text{Radius of Earth}}$$

Comparing Composition

Composition – what an object is made of.

Composition of Earth

- Rock
- Atmosphere of nitrogen and oxygen

Composition of Mercury, Venus and Mars

- Rock
- Atmosphere of a mix of gases
- Mercury has a very thin atmosphere

Composition of Jupiter, Saturn, Uranus and Neptune

- Entirely composed of gases

Comparing Gravity

Relative surface gravity – the surface gravity of one object compared with another.

$$\text{Relative Surface Gravity} \quad = \quad \frac{\text{Surface Gravity of a Space Object}}{\text{Surface Gravity of Earth}}$$

$$\text{Force = Mass} \times \text{Acceleration}$$

Gravity is important as it gives weight to an object. Weight itself is a force. Therefore:

$$\text{Weight (W) = Mass (m)} \times \text{Acceleration due to gravity (g)}$$

On Earth, the acceleration due to gravity, **g**, is 10 ms^{-2}. To calculate weight on another planet, scientists use the acceleration caused by gravity on that planet. Each planet has a different amount of gravity, and therefore the value for **g** is different.

Exam Paper 2019

Question 16

(f) The diagrams show the mass and weight of four objects (**A**, **B**, **C** and **D**) on the Earth, Earth's Moon, Jupiter and Venus.

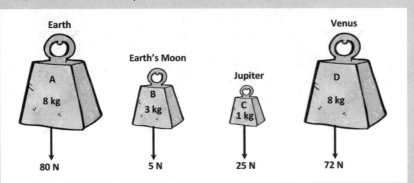

(i) Which object, **A**, **B**, **C** or **D**, has the smallest mass?
   C – 1 kg. (3)

(ii) How can you tell that the force of gravity is less on Venus than it is on the Earth?
   Object has less weight on Venus than on Earth. (3)

(g) During the Apollo 15 mission to the Moon in 1971, astronaut David Scott conducted the famous hammer and feather experiment.

   The hammer and feather were dropped at the same time from the same height and hit the surface of the Moon at the same time.

   A hammer falls much faster on Earth than it does on the Moon. Explain why.

   Gravitational force is greater on Earth than on the Moon. (3)

Sample Questions

Section A

1. The planets in our solar system are classified as either inner planets or outer planets. What do you think this classification is based on?
   How close they are to the Sun.

2. How are the compositions of outer planets similar?
   They are all gas giants made of mainly hydrogen and helium.

Section B

1. Draw a diagram of the solar system, with the planets occurring in order from the Sun, and label each object.

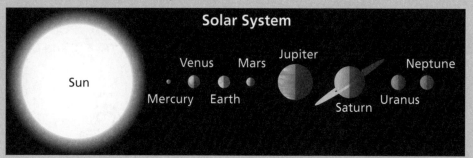

2. Assuming that the mass of Earth is 6×10^{24} kg, calculate the approximate mass of the following planets based on their relative mass:
   (a) Venus – relative mass = 0.815
   6×10^{24} kg × 0.815 = 4.89×10^{24} kg.
   (b) Mercury – relative mass = 0.0553
   6×10^{24} kg × 0.0553 = 3.31800×10^{23} kg.
   (c) Saturn – relative mass = 95.2
   6×10^{24} kg × 95.2 = 5.71200×10^{26} kg.

3. Using the table below, answer the following questions.
   (a) Which of the two planets has the greater mass?
   Mercury.
   (b) Which of the two planets has the larger radius?
   Mars.
   (c) How can Mars and Mercury have the same surface gravity even though their masses are different?

Planet	Relative Mass	Relative Radius	Relative Surface Gravity
Mars	0.107	0.532	0.38
Mercury	0.0553	0.383	0.38

   As it is related to mass and size not just mass.

20 The Universe

Learning Outcomes

1. Describe the relationships between various celestial objects including moons, asteroids, comets, planets, stars, solar systems, galaxies and space.

2. Explore a scientific model to illustrate the origin of the Universe.

aims By the end of this chapter you should:
- be able to consider the formation of the Universe
- be able to compare the different components of the Universe
- be able to outline the origins of the Universe

Galaxies

- A collection of many millions of stars, gas, dust and other objects.
- These are all held together by gravity.
- The Milky Way galaxy (our galaxy) is a spiral galaxy.

Solar Systems

Know all your definitions of what makes up our Universe.

- Consist of a star and the objects that move around it.
- Our solar system is made up of our sun, eight planets, moons, asteroids, comets, gas and dust.

Stars

- Spherical balls of burning gas that give off light and heat.
- The hottest stars are blue, and the coolest stars are red.
- Our sun is a yellow star.

Formation of a star: A Nebula is a giant cloud of gas and dust in space. As temperature and pressure within the cloud increase, nuclear fusion reactions take place and a star is formed. The life cycle of a star depends on its size.

Planets

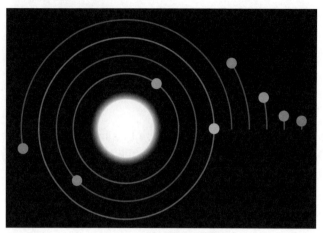

Planets travel around a star in a set path called an orbit, which is either circular or elliptical in shape.

Planets orbiting the sun

- A planet reflects light from a star and does not generate its own light.
- A planet has cleared its own orbit because any smaller objects that were in its way have been forced out of the solar system or become part of the planet.

Dwarf Planets

- A round space object that circles a star but has not cleared its own orbit.
- To be classified as a planet, a space object has to be big enough to pull in smaller space objects with its own gravity.
- Pluto is an example of a dwarf planet.

Satellites and Moons

- A satellite is an object that orbits a larger object or planet. A moon is a naturally occurring satellite.
- Most moons are solid and have no atmosphere.
- The world's first artificial satellite, Sputnik 1, was launched by the USSR in 1957.

Asteroids and Comets

- An asteroid is a small rocky object that orbits a star.
- Most asteroids have an irregular shape and in our solar system can be found in the asteroid belt between Mars and Jupiter.
- A comet is a small object composed of frozen gases, ice, rock and dust that can glow and produce a tail.

Gravity

Gravity is a force generated by all objects that attracts all other objects.

- The amount of gravity generated by an object is determined by how great or small the mass of the object is.
- Gravity is strongest at the centre of an object.

The Origins of Our Universe

The Big Bang Theory

- Before the Big Bang, over 13 billion years ago, the entire Universe was compressed into a tiny, hot mass.
- A huge expansion allowed all of the Universe's matter and energy to form.
- Gravity began to bring matter together to form stars and galaxies.
- The Universe has continued to expand ever since.
- At first the Universe expanded faster than the speed of light, before slowing down a bit.
- Therefore, light generated around the time of the Big Bang is only now catching up with us here on Earth.

Cosmic Microwave Radiation (CMB)

- Seen as important evidence for the Big Bang Theory.
- Detected by scientists using radio telescopes and satellites.
- Supporters for the Big Bang Theory state that this energy was created just after the Big Bang and has been travelling through space ever since.

exam Q

Exam Paper 2019

Question 10

Answer questions **(a)** and **(b)** by placing a tick (✔) in the correct box.

(a) A star and all of the objects that orbit it is called a

    Moon ☐   Solar system ✔   Galaxy ☐   (3)

(b) A system of billions of stars is called a

    Moon ☐   Solar system ☐   Galaxy ✔   (3)

(c) The image below shows a planet passing in front of a star. This partial eclipse is called a transit. The brightness of the light detected from the star decreases as the planet transits the star and blocks its light.

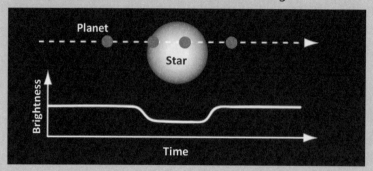

The graphs below show how the brightness of a star changed over time as two planets, **A** and **B**, transited the same star.

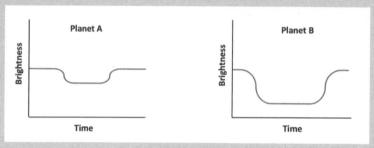

(i) Which planet, **A** or **B**, took the shortest time to transit the star?

   A. (3)

(ii) Which planet, **A** or **B**, is the largest? Give a reason for your answer.

   B: Greater decrease in brightness. (3 × 2)

Question 16

(d) The dark circles visible on the Moon's surface are craters.

Craters occur when objects with high speed strike the surface of the Moon. Examples of such objects are asteroids and comets.

What is an asteroid?

Rock orbiting the Sun. (3)

Sample Questions

Section A

1. Compare the following space objects:

   (a) Planets and dwarf planets

   A planet has cleared its own orbit, a dwarf planet has not.

   (b) Asteroids and comets

   Asteroids are mainly composed of rock while comets are mainly composed of dust and ice.

   (c) The Moon and a telecommunication satellite

   A satellite is an object that orbits a larger object or planet. The Moon is a naturally occurring satellite while the telecommunications satellite is artificial.

2. Describe our solar system by answering:

   (a) What is at the centre of our solar system?

   The Sun.

   (b) How many planets are in our solar system?

   Eight.

   (c) What other objects are found in our solar system?

   Moons, the dwarf planets, asteroids, comets and meteoroids.

3. When was the Big Bang Theory first developed and who were the scientists involved in its initial development?

   Friedmann, Lemaître, Robertson and Walker in approximately 1927.

4. Outline the evidence that supports the theory of the Big Bang.

   Hubble's Law showing the Universe expanding.

   The amount of different elements.

Section B

1. Describe the Big Bang Theory in your own words. Do you think it is a good explanation for the origins of the Universe?

   Before the Big Bang, over 13 billion years ago, the entire Universe was compressed into a tiny, hot mass.

   A huge expansion allowed all of the Universe's matter and energy to form.

   Gravity began to bring matter together to form stars and galaxies.

   The Universe has continued to expand since.

   Yes, as it is an understandable, simplified view of something that is extremely hard to understand. It explains phenomena using science that can be acted out on Earth.

21 Space Exploration

 **Learning Outcome**

8. Examine some of the current hazards and benefits of space exploration and discuss the future role and implications of space exploration in society.

 By the end of this chapter you should:
- be able to outline the history of space exploration
- discuss the impact of space exploration on life on Earth
- debate the benefits of space exploration against the hazards

Timeline

1957	1958	1961	1966
First satellite – Sputnik (USSR)	NASA Programme established (USA)	First human in space – Yuri Gagarin (USSR)	First probe on Moon – Luna 9 (USSR)

1969	1975	1977
First humans on Moon – Apollo 11 (USA)	First probe on Venus – Venera 7 (USSR)	Voyager 1 and 2 are launched (USA)

1981	1995	1998
First reusable space shuttle (USA)	First probe on Jupiter – Galileo (USA)	International Space Station (ISS)

2014	2015	2020s
First soft landing on comet – Rosetta (ESA)	First reusable rocket – Falcon 9 (SpaceX)	First humans on Mars – ITS Mission (SpaceX)

The International Space Station – a large man-made satellite orbiting Earth, where astronauts can live.

- Used for scientific research.
- Joint venture between USA, Russia, Japan, Europe and Canada.
- First piece launched in 1998. First occupied in 2000.
- Large solar panels provide power for the station.
- Orbits Earth every 90 minutes.

Areas of research on the ISS:

- Human health (investigating the effects of microgravity).
- Testing technology to help with future exploration.
- Biological sciences.
- Global climate.

Examples of Space Technologies Used on Earth

- Memory foam.
- Firefighter equipment.
- Fire-resistant paints and building materials.
- Anti-icing systems for aeroplanes.
- Infrared thermometers for monitoring health.
- Improved prosthetic limbs.

Man-made Satellites

There are currently more than 1,000 working man-made satellites in space. Some current uses of these satellites are:

- Phone and internet signals.
- Television signals.
- GPS.
- Weather forecasting.
- Digital imaging for environmental analysis.

The Future of Space Travel

- Learning more about space will help provide answers about the origins of Earth and our place in the Universe.
- New technologies developed for space can be used on Earth.
- NASA plans more manned moon missions in the future, as well as a 2020 rover mission to Mars.

Hazards of Space Exploration

Effects of space travel on the human body:

- G-force at take-off can cause unconsciousness.

- Fluid build-up, reduction of bone density and muscle mass.
- Sleep patterns affected.
- Radiation from the Sun can cause cataracts.
- Immune system is suppressed.

Ethics of Space Exploration

- Vast sums of money are spent on space travel that could be used for addressing problems on Earth.
- Space exploration adds debris to space.
- Debris can be a hazard on space missions or could also re-enter Earth's atmosphere.

Sample Questions

Section A

1. Give one reason why many people believe that space exploration contributes positively to life on Earth.

   Provides us with knowledge about the Universe that we could use on Earth.

2. How do people use information from satellites in everyday life?

   Satellite information is used for communication, weather forecasting and GPS systems, among other things.

3. How do government organisations use information from satellites?

   Government organisations can use satellites in the same way that civilians can, but also for images used in planning and military purposes.

4. What areas of research are astronauts involved in on the International Space Station?

   Human research and effects on the body, space medicine, life sciences, physical sciences, astronomy and meteorology.

5. The Rosetta Mission was the first of its kind. Explain how this project was different to other missions that looked at comets.

   This mission was the first that ever actually landed on a comet versus observing it from a distance.

6. Do you think we need to be concerned about man-made space debris? Give a reason for your answer.

   Earth's orbit may become impassable due to risk of collision with space debris.

Section B

1. Evaluate the positive and negative impacts of space exploration.

   Positives: *scientific knowledge, improvement and innovation of technologies is useful on Earth, new markets for space products.*

   Negatives: *money spent on exploration could be used elsewhere on Earth, dangerous, creates space junk.*

Chemical World

Contents

 # 22 Properties of Materials

 Learning Outcome

6. Investigate the properties of different materials including solubility, conductivity, melting points and boiling points.

aims By the end of this chapter you should:
- be able to compare physical and chemical properties of materials
- know how to explain conductivity and its associated terms and ideas
- be able to illustrate solubility and solutions

What is a Property?

A physical property is something you can observe without changing a substance.

A chemical property is the way that materials react with other materials.

 key point

A property of a material is a way of describing that material.

Physical Properties	Chemical Properties
Describe the physical characteristics of the substance.	Describe how the substance reacts with other substances.
5 senses:	**Atmospheric oxygen:**
• Texture, hardness, lustre, odour, sounds	• Flammable
• Phase at room temperature	• Non-flammable
Numerical descriptions:	• Flash point
• Density	**Water:**
• Melting/freezing point	• Dissolves, rusts, reacts
• Boiling point	**Acids:**
	• Corrosive

We can also compare the properties of substances by measuring them. The following physical properties are explored further in this chapter:

- Conductivity
- Melting point
- Boiling point
- Solubility

Conductivity

Electrical conductivity is the ability of a material to allow electricity to travel through it.

Investigate: the electrical conductivity of various materials

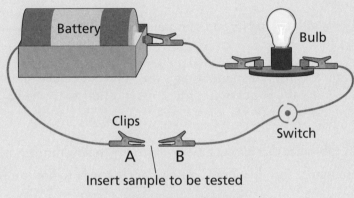

Simple electrical circuit

Method:

1. Set up circuit as shown.
2. Insert sample material to be tested between clips A and B. Test a range of different metals, wood, plastic, etc.
3. Note whether the bulb lights up.

Result:

If the bulb lights, the material is a conductor of electricity.
If the bulb does not light, the material being tested does not conduct electricity.

Thermal conductivity is the ability of a material to allow heat to travel through it.

Investigate: the thermal conductivity of various materials

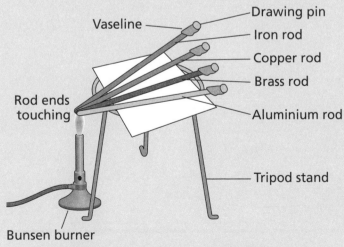

Investigation into the thermal conductivity of metals

Method:

1. Using Vaseline, stick drawing pins to the end of rods of each metal to be tested. Ensure the rods are all of equal size.

2. Set up rods on a tripod stand with the ends over a Bunsen burner, as shown in the diagram.

3. Watch as the Vaseline melts and pins fall, noting the order in which they fall.

Results:

The pin will fall first from the metal that is the best conductor of heat.
The last pin to fall is the metal that is the slowest conductor of heat.

Conductor: A substance that allows heat or electricity to flow through it.

Insulator: A substance that does not allow heat or electricity to flow through it.

Melting Point

Latent heat: The heat released or absorbed by a substance when it changes state.

Melting point: The temperature at which a substance changes from a solid state to a liquid state.

- Melting point of water = 0 °C.
- The melting point of a substance can be recorded using a melting point apparatus.
- Melting point is the same temperature at which a liquid turns into a solid when a substance is being cooled. This is the **freezing point.**

Boiling Point

Boiling point: The temperature at which a substance changes from a liquid to a gas.

- Boiling point of water = 100 °C.

Melting and Boiling Point of Water

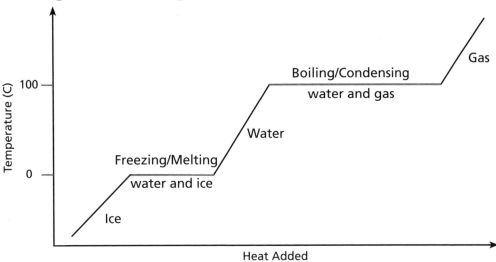

Solubility

Solubility is measured as grams of solute per 100 cm^3 of solvent. For example, the solubility of sugar in water is 204 g of sugar per 100 cm^3 of water at 20 °C.

Solute: The solid being dissolved.

Solvent: The liquid the solid is being dissolved in.

key point

SOLUBILITY
is a measure of the ability of a substance to dissolve in another substance.

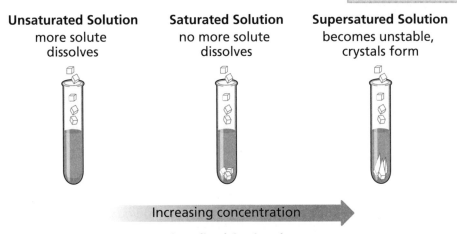

Unsaturated Solution
more solute
dissolves

Saturated Solution
no more solute
dissolves

Supersatured Solution
becomes unstable,
crystals form

Increasing concentration

Solute dissolving in solvent

Saturated solution: Contains as much dissolved solute as possible at that temperature.
Solubility can be increased by increasing the temperature or adding more solvent.

Sample Questions

Section A

1. Describe the physical properties of a plastic bottle.

   Transparent.
   Flexible.
   Elastic.

2. If 40 g of iron sulphide will dissolve in 100 cm³ of water at 20 °C, what volume of water will be needed to dissolve 120 g at the same temperature?

   3 × 100 = 300 cm³.

Section B

1. Describe an experiment to demonstrate how heat travels through a metal bar.

   Use Vaseline to stick a pin to a metal bar.
   Use forceps to put end without pin into heated Bunsen burner.
   Watch as Vaseline melts and pin drops.
   Heat has travelled through the bar and melted the Vaseline.

2. How would you measure the boiling point of methylated spirits?

   Place liquid in a flask and put over a Bunsen burner.
   Place thermometer in flask.
   Note temperature when it starts to boil.

3. Salt is spread on icy roads in winter. What property of water is changed by adding salt?

   Salt lowers the freezing point of water. It is added to roads in the hope that they will not fully freeze and become slippery.

4. Why do you think scientists use measurements of melting point as a way of determining the purity of a substance?

   The closer it is to the known melting point, the more pure it will be. Any impurities will distort.

5. How could a knowledge of boiling points be used to separate a mixture of alcohol and water?

   You could distil off the alcohol as it has a much lower boiling point than water. It would first turn to gas, which could then be trapped and cooled, forming a pure sample of alcohol.

23 Classifying Materials

4. Classify substances as elements, compounds, mixtures, metals, non-metals, solids, liquids, gases and solutions.

2. Develop and use models to describe the atomic nature of matter; demonstrate how they provide a simple way to account for the conservation of mass, changes of state, physical change, chemical change, mixtures and their separation.

aims By the end of this chapter you should:
- know how to describe matter and its different groups
- be able to compare physical and chemical reactions

Pure Substances and Mixtures

Matter is the substance or substances of which any physical object consists.

We can classify matter by organising it into different groups:

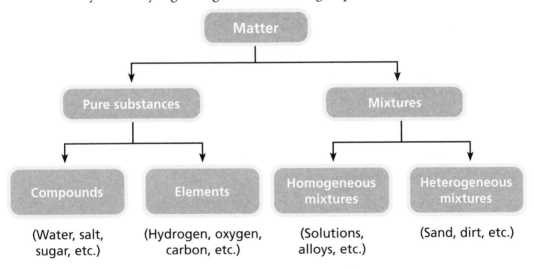

A **pure substance** is made of particles that are exactly the same as each other.

Mixtures are made of two or more different particles mixed together, e.g. seawater.

- The amount of each substance in a mixture can vary.
- No heat is needed to make a mixture.
- It is easy to separate different parts of a mixture.

Elements and Compounds

Element: A pure substance that cannot be broken down into simpler substances by chemical means.

- Elements are made of just one type of atom.
- Each element has a symbol that can be found on the Periodic Table of the elements.

Compound: A pure substance made from two or more different elements that are chemically combined.

- The elements in a compound are always present in a fixed amount.
- Heat is needed to make a compound.
- It is difficult to separate the different parts making up a compound.
- Compounds are given specific names.
- Sodium chloride is made from sodium and chloride.
- Water is made from hydrogen and oxygen.

Physical Changes and Chemical Reactions

A **physical change** is one in which no new substance is made.

Example: Freezing water changes it to ice.

- But both water and ice are the same compound. No new compounds were made in this change.

When two substances are mixed, a new substance only forms if a chemical reaction occurs.

A **chemical change** causes a new substance to form.

Example:

- Mix iron and sulphur together in a test tube.
- Heat up the test tube over a Bunsen burner.
- The iron and sulphur react together due to the energy provided by the heat of the Bunsen burner.
- Iron sulphide is formed, a new substance with its own unique properties.
- A chemical change has occurred.

Physical Changes	Chemical Changes
Crushing a can	Iron and sulphur making iron sulphide
Sugar dissolving in water	Iron rusting on a bicycle
Smashing a glass	Fireworks exploding
Ice melting	Cooking an egg
Mixing sand and water	Methane gas burning in oxygen
Chopping wood	Wood burning
Water evaporating	Milk turning sour

Sample Questions

Section A

1. What is the difference between a mixture and a compound?
   A mixture is made of two or more different particles mixed together. A compound is a pure substance made from two or more different elements that are chemically combined.

2. Give symbols of the following elements:
   (a) hydrogen – *H.*
   (b) carbon – *C.*
   (c) copper – *Cu.*
   (d) sulphur – *S.*
   (e) iron – *Fe.*
   (f) nitrogen – *N.*
   (g) zinc – *Zn.*
   (h) aluminium – *Al.*
   (i) sodium – *Na.*
   (j) chlorine – *Cl.*
   (k) silver – *Ag.*
   (l) gold – *Au.*

3. List three physical changes and three chemical changes.
   Physical: crushing, melting, boiling.
   Chemical: burning, rusting, cooking.

Section B

1. Think of a compound that is part of your daily life and describe how you use it.
   Sodium chloride (salt) is put on food.

2. Is salt water a pure substance? Explain your answer.
   No, it is a mixture of salt dissolved in water.

3. Why is cooking an egg considered a chemical change and not a physical one?
   Chemical bonds are broken and new ones are made.

24 Mixtures

 **Learning Outcome**

4. Classify substances as elements, compounds, mixtures, metals, non-metals, solids, liquids, gases and solutions.

 aims By the end of this chapter you should:

- consider different types of solutions and how to separate mixtures

Solutions

Soluble substances are able to dissolve in a liquid.

- **Example:** sugar in water.

Insoluble substances do not dissolve in a liquid.

- **Example:** sand in water.
- Sand particles cannot fill the gaps between the water molecules.

key point

A **MIXTURE** is made of two or more different particles mixed together.

Solute: A substance that dissolves in another substance.

Solvent: A substance that dissolves other substances.

Solution: A mixture of two or more substances.

Solution = Solvent + Solute

Solutions		
Diluted solution	**Concentrated solution**	**Saturated solution**
Has very little solute in it	Has a lot of solute in it	Has the maximum amount of solute in it
Can dissolve a lot more solute	Can dissolve a little more solute	Cannot dissolve any more solute

Separating Mixtures

 key point

Mixtures form without any chemical changes taking place. Therefore, it is possible to separate them into the different materials that make them up.

1. Filtration

A good method of separation for solids that are insoluble in water.

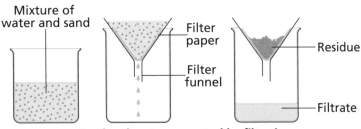

Mixture of water and sand — Filter paper — Filter funnel — Residue — Filtrate

Sand and water separated by filtration

2. Evaporation

Appropriate for solids that are soluble in water (e.g. salt).

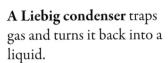

Solution of water and salt — Solution is heated to boiling point for the liquid to evaporate — Solid particles of salt remain after liquid evaporates

Salt separated from water by evaporation

3. Distillation

- Useful when you want to keep the liquid part after separation.
- It can be used to separate two miscible liquids (liquids that mix together) with different boiling points.

A Liebig condenser traps gas and turns it back into a liquid.

- Inner tube allows gas to travel through.
- Outer tube lets cold water travel through, which cools the gas and condenses it back to a liquid.

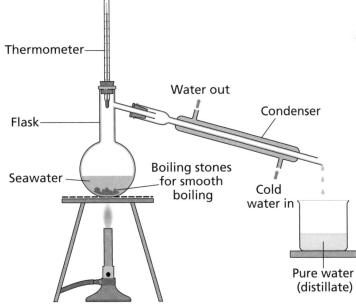

Thermometer — Water out — Condenser — Flask — Seawater — Boiling stones for smooth boiling — Cold water in — Pure water (distillate)

Salt and water separated by distillation

4. Chromatography

A way of separating mixtures made up of many different parts.

- **Example:** Black ink (which is made of many different coloured inks mixed together).

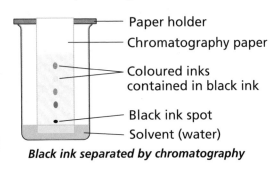

Paper holder — Chromatography paper — Coloured inks contained in black ink — Black ink spot — Solvent (water)

Black ink separated by chromatography

- Chromatography separates these inks because different ink particles travel different distances up the chromatography paper.

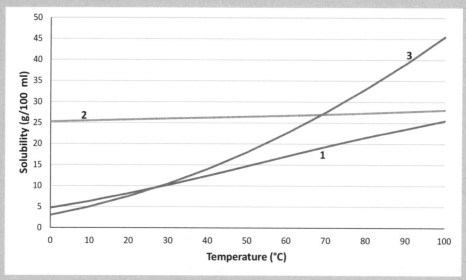

exam
Q

Sample Paper 2019

Question 3

A group of students investigated how solubility in water changes with temperature for solid compounds **1**, **2** and **3**. The graph below shows the results obtained.

(a) Hot water was needed during this investigation.

Name an instrument used to heat water in the laboratory.

Bunsen burner.

(b) Describe one safety precaution which should be taken when heating water in the laboratory.

Wear safety goggles.

(c) Which compound shows the greatest increase in solubility from 0 °C to 100 °C?

The general trend for solids is that solubility increases with temperature.

(d) On the graph, circle the point where compound **2** has the same solubility as compound **3**.

Mark intersection of lines 2 and 3.

(e) State one advantage of presenting scientific data using a graph.

Easy for interpretation and comparison of data.

Sample Questions

Section A

1. Why do you think that only a certain amount of solute can dissolve in a fixed volume of solvent?

   As capacity to absorb is reached, there is no more room.

2. Give examples of three different mixtures that can be separated by filtration.

   Dirt and water.

   Pebbles and water.

   Cornflakes and milk.

3. What happens to the water when you heat a mixture of salt and water above 100 °C?

   It evaporates.

Section B

1. How does a Liebig condenser work?

   A Liebig condenser condenses vapours that pass through the centre tube. It is cooled with water that passes in the outer tube turning gas back to liquid for collection.

2. Give three mixtures that could be separated using a Liebig condenser.

   Salt and water.

   Water and alcohol.

   Different oils.

3. Do you think increasing the temperature of a solvent would change the amount of solute it could dissolve? Describe a simple experiment to investigate this.

   Yes, as the solvent particles would spread out creating more space for the solute.

   Add salt to water at different temperatures.

4. Can distillation only be used to separate soluble solids and liquids? Find out some other uses of distillation.

   No, insoluble solids or liquids may be separated using distillation, e.g. alcoholic drinks.

5. Give two uses of chromatography.

   Forensic testing to catch criminals.

   Food testing, e.g. in the horse meat scandal.

Learning Outcomes

1. Investigate whether mass is unchanged when chemical and physical changes take place.

2. Develop and use models to describe the atomic nature of matter; demonstrate how they provide a simple way to account for the conservation of mass, changes of state, physical change, chemical change, mixtures and their separation.

aims By the end of this chapter you should:
- consider matter and its different states
- discuss the changes of states of matter
- explain the conservation of mass

What is Matter?

- Almost everything in the world is comprised of matter.
- Three things not made of matter: time, heat, gravity.

Mass: The amount of matter in an object.

Volume: The amount of space an object takes up.

 key point

MATTER is anything that occupies space and has mass.

Measuring Matter

Matter is measured in milligrams (mg), grams (g) and kilograms (kg).

1 g = 1000 mg

1 kg = 1000 g

1 tonne = 1000 kg

Mass and Weight

Mass ≠ Weight

Mass	Weight
• Amount of matter in a substance	• Weight = mass × force of gravity
• Remains constant	• Changes with the force of gravity
• Unit = kilogram	• Unit = newton

Example: My <u>weight</u> on Earth is around 560 N.

My <u>weight</u> on the Moon is around 90 N.

My <u>mass</u> is always 56 kg!

Weight = Mass × Gravity

Know the difference between mass and weight as they appear on Earth and in space also.

The Atomic Nature of Matter

Atoms are tiny particles that are the building blocks of matter.

Atoms contain even smaller subatomic particles that are difficult to separate from each other.

Molecules form when atoms join together.

- Water = 2 hydrogen atoms + 1 oxygen atom.

Hydrogen   Hydrogen

H   H

O

Oxygen
Water molecule

Particles of matter refer to both atoms and molecules.

How particles in an object move in relation to one another accounts for the **state of matter** of the object.

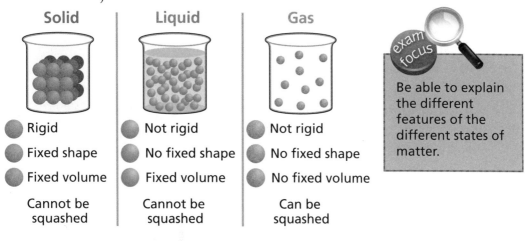

Solid	Liquid	Gas
Rigid	Not rigid	Not rigid
Fixed shape	No fixed shape	No fixed shape
Fixed volume	Fixed volume	No fixed volume
Cannot be squashed	Cannot be squashed	Can be squashed

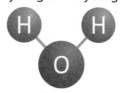

Be able to explain the different features of the different states of matter.

Solid	Liquid	Gas
Particles are tightly packed together.	Particles stay close to one another but can move past each other.	Particles move in all directions and bounce off one another.
Particles can vibrate but stay close to one another.	Particles are able to flow.	Gas will spread out to fill any container it is held in.
Example: ice	Example: water	Example: water vapour

Changes of State

The state of matter of an object depends on the amount of heat energy it has. Matter will change its state depending on how much it is heated or cooled.

Changes of State		
Solid	Liquid	Gas
Ice	Water	Water vapour
(Melting) ⟶	(Evaporating) ⟶	
	⟵ (Freezing)	⟵ (Condensing)

Changing state with pressure

- Carbon dioxide is normally a gas at room temperature.
- Fire extinguishers are filled by putting carbon dioxide under high pressure.
- Pressure causes carbon dioxide to change from a gas to a liquid.
- It remains as a liquid in the cylinder until it is released.
- At release it changes back to a gas and smothers the fire.

Conservation of mass

A **closed system** prevents anything already in the system from leaving and does not allow anything else to get into the system.

- When it appears that the total mass of a system has either increased or decreased, it must be because the system is not closed.
- In a closed system the total number of atoms is fixed, even if there are chemical or physical changes.
- The mass stays the same.

> **key point**
>
> In a closed system the total mass will remain the same even if there are physical or chemical changes.

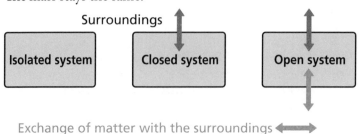

Surroundings

Isolated system   Closed system   Open system

Exchange of matter with the surroundings ⟷
Exchange of energy with the surroundings ⟷

There are generally three types of systems.		
Open system	Closed system	Isolated system
An *open system* can exchange mass and energy, usually in the form of heat, with its surroundings.	A *closed system* allows the transfer of energy (heat) but not mass.	An *isolated system* does not allow the transfer of either mass or energy.

Exam Paper 2019

Question 15

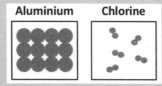

The diagrams above show the arrangement of particles in the elements aluminium and chlorine at room temperature.

(d) What evidence is there in the diagrams to support the classification of these substances as elements?

The particles making them up are the same. (3)

(e) Which of these elements is a solid at room temperature? Justify your answer.

Aluminium: Particles are close together. (2 × 3)

Sample Paper 2019

Question 6

In the diagrams below, circles of different colours are used to represent atoms of different elements.

Complete the table below for the substances shown in diagrams **A** to **E**.

In each case, state whether the diagram represents a solid, a liquid or a gas.

Also state whether the diagram represents an element, a compound or a mixture.

(Some parts of the table are already completed for you.)

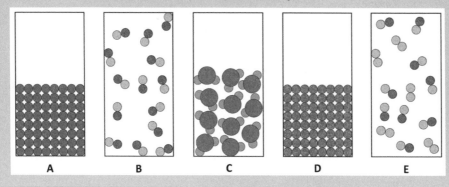

Diagram	Solid, liquid or gas	Element, compound or mixture
A	*Solid*	**Mixture**
B	*Gas*	*Compound*
C	*Liquid*	*Compound*
D	**Solid**	*Element*
E	*Gas*	*Mixture*

Sample Questions

Section A

1. Explain what is happening to the particles in a solid while it is melting.

   Particles have more energy and vibrate faster. The order structure breaks down.

2. Explain what is happening to the particles in a liquid while it is boiling.

   Particles are given more energy and move faster and faster, expanding the liquid. Liquids evaporate faster as they heat up and more particles have enough energy to break away. The particles need energy to overcome the attractions between them.

3. What is the difference between mass and weight?

   Mass is the actual amount of material contained in an object. Weight is the force exerted by gravity on the object. (weight = mass × gravity)

4. Why do you think it is important to have a standardised system of weights and measures around the world?

   So comparisons and references can be made both in science and everyday life.

5. How does an understanding of the atomic nature of matter help to explain changes in state?

   Allows us to see what is happening to the particles as changes occur under different conditions.

6. When water freezes it expands. Does this mean that its mass increases? Explain your answer.

   No, as it does not change the amount of atoms in the water.

7. Give two everyday examples of:

   (a) Melting
       Ice turning to water, melting of butter.

   (b) Freezing
       Water turning to ice, solidification of candle wax.

   (c) Evaporating
       Drying clothes, cooling of tea.

Section B

1. Explain the difference between the three states of matter: solid, liquid, and gas.

   Solid: *A substance that retains its size and shape without a container; a substance whose molecules cannot move freely except to vibrate.*

   Liquid: *A substance that flows and keeps no definite shape because its molecules are loosely packed and constantly moving. It takes the shape of its container but maintains constant volume.*

   Gas: *A substance that can only be contained if it is fully surrounded by a container (or held together by gravitational pull); a substance whose molecules have negligible intermolecular interactions and can move freely.*

26 Acids and Bases

 **Learning Outcome**

8. Investigate reactions between acids and bases; use indicators and the pH scale.

 aims By the end of this chapter you should:
- be able to classify acids and bases
- know how to explain the use of indicators
- be able to outline a titration experiment

Acids

 **exam focus**

- Have a pH of 1–6.
- They have a sour taste.
- Concentrated acids are very **corrosive**.
  — **Example:** Lemon juice.

Know the key features of acids and bases.

Corrosive: Damages substances that it comes in contact with.

Bases

- Have a pH of 8–14.
- Have a soapy feel when they react with water.
- Bases that dissolve in water are called alkalis.
- Concentrated bases are very **corrosive**.
  — **Example:** Toothpaste.

The pH Scale is a measure of how acidic or basic a substance is.

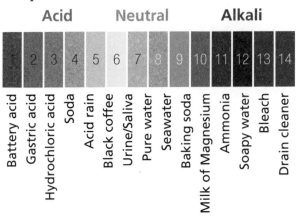

The pH scale

Indicators

Indicator: A substance which, by changing colour, can show whether another substance is an acid or a base.

- Used to test for acids and bases.
- **Examples** include litmus indicator, universal indicator, methyl orange.

Acids turn blue litmus paper red.

Bases turn red litmus paper blue.

Natural indicators: Pigments from plants, fruits, and vegetables can be used to make indicator solutions.

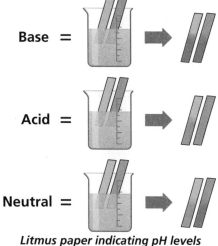

Base =

Acid =

Neutral =

Litmus paper indicating pH levels

- Some pigments show a range of colours in acids and bases of different concentrations.
- Some pigments only change colours in either acids or bases.

Investigate: using red cabbage indicator

Method:

1. Chop red cabbage into small pieces.
2. Pour boiling water over red cabbage and leave to soften. Water will turn purple with time.
3. Strain purple water with a sieve and collect in a clear container.
4. Place a small amount of lemon juice, bicarbonate of soda and water into separate clear jars.
5. Use a dropper to add a small amount of cabbage water to each.
6. Observe any changes.

Neutralisation

- A salt is a substance where the hydrogen of an acid is replaced by a metal ion.

Neutralisation reactions

Acid-base reactions, or neutralisation reactions, form water and an ionic compound (a 'salt').

key point

NEUTRALISATION

A reaction where an acid and a base react to form a neutral solution of a salt and water.

HCl(aq)	+	NaOH(aq)	→	NaCl(aq)	+	H$_2$O(l)
Acid		Base		Salt		Water

In this reaction the hydrogen of the hydrochloric acid is replaced by a sodium ion from the sodium hydroxide to form the salt sodium chloride.

Everyday neutralisation reactions:

1. Bee sting (acid) ➜ Baking powder (base)

2. Teeth bacteria (acid) ➜ Toothpaste (base)

Titration

Titration is a method used to investigate reactions between substances, including the neutralisation reaction between an acid and a base.

- A **pipette** is used to measure an exact volume of base to be added to a conical flask.
- A **burette** is used to measure the volume of acid to be added to the base in order to neutralise it.
- An **indicator** is added to the conical flask.
- As the acid is added, the molecules of base in the flask react with the acid molecules.
- At the endpoint of titration, the last drop of acid neutralises the remaining molecules of base.
- The indicator changes colour at the point of neutralisation.

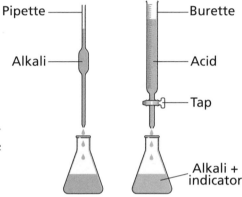

Titration used to investigate neutralisation

Exam Paper 2019

Question 6

A student carried out an experiment to investigate the reaction between an acid and a base.

A pH indicator and a thermometer were used to monitor changes in pH and temperature during the reaction.

(a) Name a pH indicator the student could have used during this investigation.

Methyl orange/litmus. (3)

(b) What colour is this indicator when placed in acid?

Red. (3)

(c) When an acid and a base react, they neutralise each other to produce a neutral solution.

On the pH scale, what number represents a neutral solution?

7. (3)

(d) The student noted a rise in temperature as the acid-base reaction took place.

Is this an example of an endothermic or an exothermic reaction?

Exothermic. (3)

(e) The diagram shows an energy profile diagram for the reaction between an acid and a base.

On the diagram, show the activation energy for this reaction.

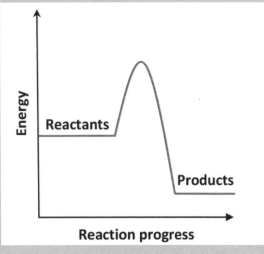

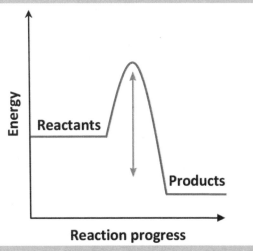

(3)

Sample Paper 2019

Question 11

Citric acid is a chemical found in lemons and some other fruits.

It is a white crystalline solid when pure.

Solid citric acid may be dissolved in water to make a citric acid solution.

(a) Describe how to make up a solution which contains 5 g of citric acid dissolved in 100 ml of water. As part of your description, name each piece of equipment you would use.

(A labelled diagram may help your answer.)

Place weigh boat on mass balance and zero it.

Add 5 g of citric acid using a spatula.

Rinse equipment to be used with distilled water.

Add water to beaker and stir in citric acid.

Rinse any residue into beaker using a wash bottle of distilled water.

Pour beaker contents into a 100 ml volumetric flask.

Top up to 100 ml using distilled water.

Baking soda is another white solid compound. Its chemical name is sodium hydrogen carbonate. It is often used in making bread and cake.

When baking soda is added to a test tube of citric acid solution, fizzing occurs and a gas is produced.

(b) A student holding the test tube notices that it cools down during the reaction.

Is this reaction an example of an endothermic or an exothermic reaction? Explain your answer.

Endothermic – steady drop in temperature as heat is taken in.

This reaction is also an example of an acid-base reaction.

When baking soda is added to a test tube of citric acid solution, the chemicals react and the pH of the solution changes.

(c) Would you expect the pH of the solution in the test tube to increase or decrease during the reaction? Explain your answer.

Increase as you are adding a more basic product.

(d) Describe how you could investigate how pH changes during the reaction.

Use a clean pH meter and monitor the pH over regular time intervals until they become consistent.

Sample Questions

Section A

1. 'Concentrated bases are just as harmful as acids.' Discuss.

   They are both corrosive and therefore harmful.

2. Name two substances that are produced by a neutralisation reaction between an acid and a base. What method of separation can be used to separate these two substances?

    Salt and water produced.

    Can be separated by evaporation.

3. At what number of the pH scale do you think the following substances lie:

    (a) Lemon juice

     2.

    (b) Soap

     9.

    (c) Window cleaner

     8.

    (d) Oven cleaner

     5.

    (e) Acid rain

     4.

4. Name all the laboratory equipment needed to carry out a titration to neutralise an acid with a base.

    Equipment: burette, pipette, measuring flask, beakers, measuring cylinder and a burette stand.

Section B

1. A student found that two indigestion remedies neutralised different volumes of the same acid. They found that:

    — One tablet of remedy A neutralised a very large volume of acid and produced a large volume of carbon dioxide.

    — One tablet of remedy B neutralised a smaller volume of acid and produced a smaller volume of carbon dioxide.

    Explain which indigestion remedy you would recommend and why.

    B, as indigestion does not have a large amount of acid.

2. A titration was used to find the volume of hydrochloric acid needed to neutralise 25 cm^3 of sodium hydroxide. A group of students obtained these results: 12.5 cm^3, 15 cm^3, and 11.4 cm^3. Their teacher suggested they needed to repeat the titration. Why do you think their teacher suggested this?

    There is a result that is too different from the others, which may indicate a mistake (15 cm^3).

3. Choose an indigestion remedy that can be bought in a pharmacy. Find out what base is used.

    Rennie Spearmint tablets contain two antacids called calcium carbonate and magnesium carbonate.

27 Structure of the Atom

⇨ **Learning Outcome**

3. Describe and model the structure of the atom in terms of the nucleus, protons, neutrons and electrons; comparing mass and charge of protons, neutrons and electrons.

 By the end of this chapter you should:

- outline the structure of an atom
- recognise atomic numbers, mass numbers isotopes and ions
- be able to use the Bohr model of atoms

The Atom

Atoms: The smallest part of an element.

- Mostly made up of empty space.
- Have a dense nucleus in their centre where almost all the matter is held.

Subatomic particles: The particles that atoms are made of.

An **ELEMENT** is a substance that cannot be broken down into simpler substances by chemical means.

Protons, Electrons and Neutrons

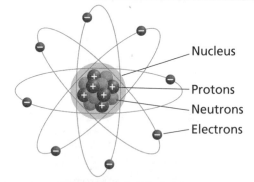

Nucleus
Protons
Neutrons
Electrons

The structure of an atom

Particle	Proton	Electron	Neutron
Location	Nucleus	Electron cloud	Nucleus
Mass	1 a.m.u.	$\frac{1}{1836}$ a.m.u.	1 a.m.u.
Charge	+1 (positive)	−1 (negative)	0 (neutral)

a.m.u. = atomic mass unit = 1.66×10^{-30} g

Calculating the number of protons, electrons and neutrons

Every element listed on the Periodic Table has two numbers listed with it.

The atomic number: The number of protons in an atom's nucleus (smaller number).

The mass number: The combined total of protons and neutrons in its nucleus (bigger number).

If an atom is neutral, then there is the same number of electrons as protons in the atom.

Subtract the atomic number from the mass number to find the number of neutrons in an atom.

Isotopes

Isotopes are atoms of the same element that have different numbers of neutrons in the nucleus.

- This is why most Periodic Tables do not give the mass number as a simple whole number.

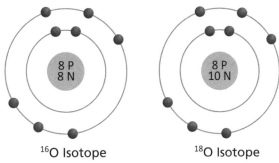

^{16}O Isotope ^{18}O Isotope

Oxygen isotopes

Example:

Isotope	Carbon 12	Carbon 14
Atomic number	6	6
Number of protons	6	6
Mass number	12	14
Number of neutrons	12 – 6 = 6	14 – 6 = 8

Atomic Mass is the average mass of the atoms of that element. Because there is a small number of the heavier carbon-14 isotope, the atomic mass of carbon is 12.

Ions

Ions are atoms that have lost or gained electrons.

- If the number of protons in an atom changes, it becomes an atom of a different element.
- This can only happen through nuclear reaction.
- If the number of neutrons changes, the atom does not become a different element, just an isotope.

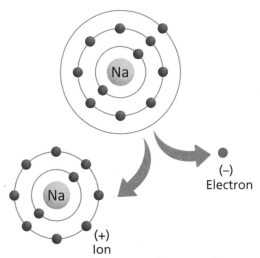

(–) Electron

(+) Ion

A sodium atom losing one electron to become a sodium cation (positively charged ion)

- If the number of electrons changes, the atom does not become a different element, it becomes an ion.

Anions are elements that have gained electrons and have a negative charge.

Cations are elements that have lost electrons and have a positive charge.

Electronic Structure of an Atom

A **Bohr model** is a diagram that helps explain the structure of an atom.

- Named after the Danish scientist Niels Bohr, who first suggested it in 1912.

The electron cloud is divided into areas called **energy levels or shells**. Electrons have a definite amount of energy in these energy levels.

As the number of electrons in an atom increases, more energy levels are added.

- Lowest energy level can hold two electrons.
- Next two energy levels can hold up to eight electrons.
- The next energy level can hold more electrons again.
- This model works well for the first 20 elements in the Periodic Table.

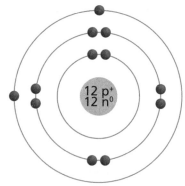

12 p^+
12 n^0

Magnesium

Bohr model of a magnesium atom

exam
Q

Sample Paper 2019

Question 8

(a) Match each of the following sub-atomic particles to their descriptions in the table below.

Electron   Neutron   Proton

Description	Particle
Positively charged	*Proton*
Negatively charged	*Electron*
No charge	*Neutron*

(b) Complete the table below, using the Periodic Table of the elements to predict the ratio of atoms and the chemical formula for each of the compounds listed.

You should refer to page 79 of the *Formulae and Tables* booklet when answering this question.

The first row is completed for you.

Compound	First element	Second element	Ratio	Formula
Positively charged	Hydrogen (H)	Oxygen (O)	2 : 1	H_2O
Negatively charged	Magnesium (Mg)	Chlorine (Cl)	1 : 2	$MgCl_2$
No charge	Nitrogen (N)	Hydrogen (H)	1 : 3	NH_3

Sample Questions

Section A

1. Use the Periodic Table to find out how many protons, neutrons and electrons are in an atom of each of the following elements:
   (a) Potassium
   19 protons, 19 electrons, 20 neutrons.
   (b) Hydrogen
   1 proton, 1 electron, 0 neutrons.
   (c) Iron
   26 protons, 26 electrons, 30 neutrons.

2. Calcium has an atomic number of 20. Give the arrangement of the electrons in its atom.
   2, 8, 8, 2.

3. Explain how an ion forms.
   Ions are formed when atoms lose or gain electrons.

4. What are isotopes?
   Atoms of the same element that contain equal numbers of protons but different numbers of neutrons in their nuclei.

Section B

1. Carbon-14 is an isotope of carbon which is very important in archaeology. Find out what it is used for.
   Used in ageing items (carbon dating).

 **Learning Outcome**

5. Use the Periodic Table to predict the ratio of atoms in compounds of two elements.

 By the end of this chapter you should:

● become familiar with the Periodic Table and interpret its constituent parts

The Periodic Table

● The first 98 elements are said to be naturally occurring.
● Elements with atomic numbers higher than 98 have been made by scientists.
● Elements 113, 115, 117 and 118 were discovered in 2015 and given the temporary names Uut, Uup, Uus and Uuo until their actual names and symbols are agreed upon.

How is the Periodic Table organised?

● Arranged in order of increasing atomic number.
● Elements with the same number of electrons in their outer shell are in the same column (called **groups**).
● Elements in a group have similar properties.
● Each group has its own name, e.g. group 1 are the alkali metals, group 2 are the alkaline earth metals, etc.

Know the overview of the Periodic Table.

Periodic Table of the Elements

Atomic Number → 1
→ Symbol
H
Name → Hydrogen
1.008
→ Atomic Weight

State of matter at room temperature
(Colour of name)
GAS LIQUID SOLID UNKNOWN

■ Unknown chemical properties

1 IA	2 IIA											13 IIIA	14 IVA	15 VA	16 VIA	17 VIIA	18 VIIIA
1 H Hydrogen 1.008																	2 He Helium 4.0026
3 Li Lithium 6.94	4 Be Beryllium 9.0122											5 B Boron 2-3	6 C Carbon 12.011	7 N Nitrogen 14.007	8 O Oxygen 15.999	9 F Fluorine 18.998	10 Ne Neon 20.180
11 Na Sodium 22.98976928	12 Mg Magnesium 24.305	3 IIIB	4 IVB	5 VB	6 VIB	7 VIIB	8 VIIIB	9 VIIIB	10 VIIIB	11 IB	12 IIB	13 Al Aluminium 26.982	14 Si Silicon 28.085	15 P Phosphorus 30.974	16 S Sulphur 32.06	17 Cl Chlorine 35.45	18 Ar Argon 39.948
19 K Potassium 39.0983	20 Ca Calcium 40.078	21 Sc Scandium 44.955908	22 Ti Titanium 47.867	23 V Vanadium 50.9415	24 Cr Chromium 51.9961	25 Mn Manganese 54.938044	26 Fe Iron 55.845	27 Co Cobalt 58.9331	28 Ni Nickel 58.6934	29 Cu Copper 63.546	30 Zn Zinc 65.38	31 Ga Gallium 69.723	32 Ge Germanium 72.630	33 As Arsenic 74.922	34 Se Selenium 78.971	35 Br Bromine 79.904	36 Kr Krypton 83.798
37 Rb Rubidium 85.4678	38 Sr Strontium 87.62	39 Y Yttrium 88.90584	40 Zr Zirconium 91.224	41 Nb Niobium 92.90637	42 Mo Molybdenum 95.95	43 Tc Technetium (98)	44 Ru Ruthenium 101.07	45 Rh Rhodium 102.91	46 Pd Palladium 106.42	47 Ag Silver 107.87	48 Cd Cadmium 112.41	49 In Indium 114.82	50 Sn Tin 118.71	51 Sb Antimony 121.76	52 Te Tellurium 127.60	53 I Iodine 126.90	54 Xe Xenon 131.29
55 Cs Caesium 132.90545196	56 Ba Barium 137.33	57-71 Lanthanides	72 Hf Hafnium 178.49	73 Ta Tantalum 180.94788	74 W Tungsten 183.84	75 Re Rhenium 186.21	76 Os Osmium 190.23	77 Ir Iridium 192.22	78 Pt Platinum 195.08	79 Au Gold 196.97	80 Hg Mercury 200.59	81 Tl Thallium 204.38	82 Pb Lead 207.2	83 Bi Bismuth 208.98	84 Po Polonium (209)	85 At Astatine (210)	86 Rn Radon (222)
87 Fr Francium (223)	88 Ra Radium (226)	89-103 Actinides	104 Rf Rutherfordium (267)	105 Db Dubnium (268)	106 Sg Seaborgium (269)	107 Bh Bohrium (270)	108 Hs Hassium (277)	109 Mt Meitnerium (278)	110 Ds Darmstadtium (281)	111 Rg Roentgenium (282)	112 Cn Copernicium (285)	113 Nh Nihonium (286)	114 Fl Flerovium (289)	115 Mc Moscovium (290)	116 Lv Livermorium (293)	117 Ts Tennessine (294)	118 Og Oganesson (294)

57 La Lanthanum 138.91	58 Ce Cerium 140.12	59 Pr Praseodymium 140.91	60 Nd Neodymium 144.24	61 Pm Promethium (145)	62 Sm Samarium 150.36	63 Eu Europium 151.96	64 Gd Gadolinium 157.25	65 Tb Terbium 158.93	66 Dy Dysprosium 162.50	67 Ho Holmium 164.93	68 Er Erbium 167.26	69 Tm Thulium 168.93	70 Yb Ytterbium 173.05	71 Lu Lutetium 174.97
89 Ac Actinium (227)	90 Th Thorium 232.04	91 Pa Protactinium 231.04	92 U Uranium 238.03	93 Np Neptunium (237)	94 Pu Plutonium (244)	95 Am Americium (243)	96 Cm Curium (247)	97 Bk Berkelium (247)	98 Cf Californium (251)	99 Es Einsteinium (252)	100 Fm Fermium (257)	101 Md Mendelevium (258)	102 No Nobelium (259)	103 Lr Lawrencium (266)

Subcategory in the metal–metalloid–nonmetal trend (colour of background)
■ Alkali metals ■ Transition metals ■ Metalloids ■ Noble gases
■ Alkaline earth metals ■ Lanthanides ■ Post-transition metals ■ Reactive nonmetals
■ Actinides

Main Groups and Their Properties

Group 1: Alkali Metals, e.g. Lithium, Sodium, Potassium

- Are soft (they can be cut with a knife).
- Have relatively low melting points.
- Have low densities.

Group 2: Alkaline Earth Metals, e.g. Beryllium, Magnesium, Calcium

- Are less reactive than alkali metals.
- Are good conductors of heat and electricity.

Group 7: Halogens, e.g. Fluorine, Chlorine, Bromine, Iodine

- Have seven electrons in their outer shell.
- React with metals to produce salts (e.g. chlorine reacts with sodium).
- Become less reactive as you move down the group.

Group 0: Noble Gases, e.g. Helium, Neon, Argon

- Have low boiling points.
- Have low densities.

Metals and Non-metals

Physical properties of metals

- Hard and dense.
- Electrical conductors.
- Heat conductors.
- Shiny.
- Sonorous.
- Ductile (can be drawn out into wire).
- Malleable (can be hammered into different shapes).
- Have a high melting point.

Corrosion refers to the deterioration of a metal as a result of chemical reactions between it and the surrounding environment.

- **Example:** When metals react with oxygen in the air. Iron becomes iron oxide (i.e. rust), which is brittle and unsuitable for use.

Investigate: rusting

Method:

1. Set up the test tubes as shown in the diagram.

2. Leave the test tubes for a few days and observe if rust forms.

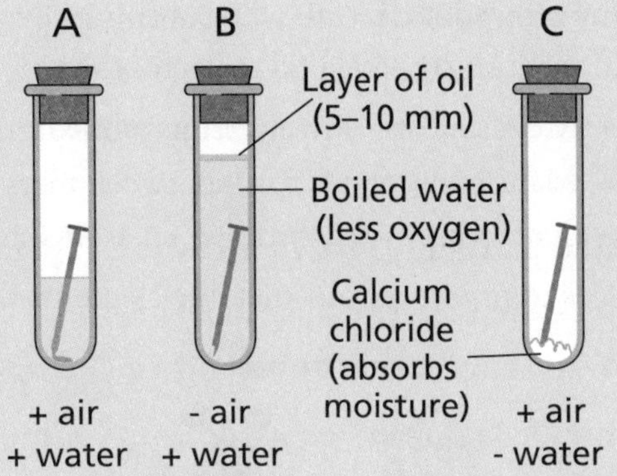

Results:

A B C

Layer of oil (5–10 mm)

Boiled water (less oxygen)

Calcium chloride (absorbs moisture)

+ air + water   - air + water   + air - water

- The nail in test tube B does not rust because the nail was exposed only to water and no air. Similarly, the nail in test tube C does not rust because water is not present.
- The nail in test tube A rusts because the nail was exposed to both air and water.
- This shows that for rusting to occur, both air and water are necessary.

Non-metals usually:

- Have low boiling and melting points.
- Poor conductors of heat.
- Poor conductors of electricity.
- Dull (not shiny).

Metalloids are elements that are very useful because under some conditions they behave like metals and conduct electricity, and under others they can behave like non-metals.

Predicting Formulae

The molecular formula gives the total number of atoms in each element in a molecule.

- **Example:** Molecular formula for glucose is $C_6H_{12}O_6$.
- This means that one molecule of glucose comprises six carbon atoms, 12 hydrogen atoms and six oxygen atoms.

The octet rule is used to explain why most of the first 20 elements in the Periodic Table bond in order to have eight electrons in their outermost shell.

- Atoms are more stable when they have a full outer shell.
- They can achieve this by giving away electrons, receiving electrons or sharing electrons with another atom.

Compounds

Ionic compounds form when atoms lose or gain electrons to form ions. The oppositely charged ions are attracted to each other.

- Metals mostly lose electrons while non-metals mostly receive or share electrons.
- Many compounds form between metals and non-metals.

Covalent compounds form when atoms share electrons.

- Atoms of two non-metallic elements share electrons from their outer energy levels.

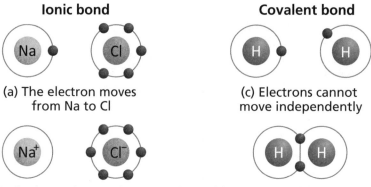

Ionic bond

(a) The electron moves from Na to Cl

(b) Positively charged Na and negatively charged Cl attract each other and are electronically bonded together

Covalent bond

(c) Electrons cannot move independently

(d) The atoms form bonds by sharing electrons

Ionic compound example

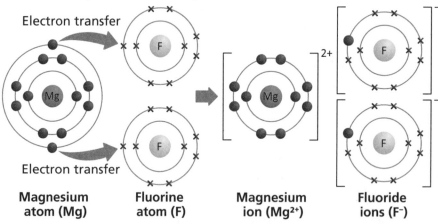

Electron transfer

Electron transfer

| Magnesium atom (Mg) | Fluorine atom (F) | Magnesium ion (Mg²⁺) | Fluoride ions (F⁻) |

Ionic compound between a magnesium atom and two fluorine atoms

Magnesium and fluorine combine in a 1 : 2 ratio to form MgF_2 when a magnesium atom gives one electron to each fluorine atom.

Covalent compound example

Carbon and hydrogen combine in a 1 : 4 ratio to form CH_4 (i.e. methane), when each hydrogen atom shares one electron with a carbon atom and the carbon atom shares one electron with each hydrogen atom.

Naming compounds

When a metal and a non-metal form to make a compound, the compound is given the **name of the metal** followed by the **non-metal** with the **ending changed to -ide**.

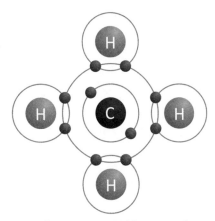

Covalent compound between four hydrogen atoms and one carbon atom, forming methane

- **Example:** Sodium and chlorine form sodium chloride.
- **Example:** Magnesium and oxygen form magnesium oxide.

Chemical Equations

When molecules react, atoms simply rearrange into new compounds; they are not created or destroyed. **The mass is always conserved.**

Example:

$$HCl + NaOH \rightarrow NaCl + H_2O$$

Reactants	Number of Atoms	Products	Number of Atoms
H	2	H	2
Cl	1	Cl	1
Na	1	Na	1
Na	1	Na	1

Exam Paper 2019

Question 15

The Periodic Table was developed by Dmitri Mendeleev. It was published 150 years ago in 1869.

To celebrate the International Year of the Periodic Table, The European Chemical Society has designed a new kind of Periodic Table called the '90 Elements that make up everything'.

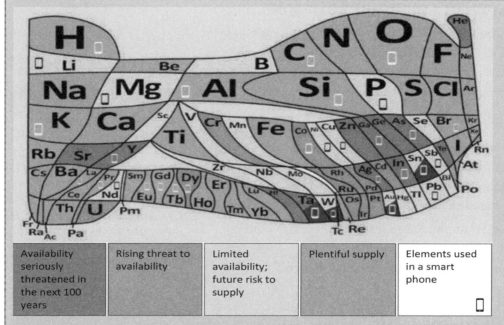

Availability seriously threatened in the next 100 years	Rising threat to availability	Limited availability; future risk to supply	Plentiful supply	Elements used in a smart phone

The table has been drawn so that the area occupied by each element indicates how much of that element is in the Earth's crust and atmosphere.

(a) From the table, identify a gas which is a component of the Earth's atmosphere and which is in plentiful supply.

Nitrogen/Oxygen. (3)

(b) Why should the use of the gas helium (He) in birthday balloons be avoided?

Availability is limited. (3)

(c) The element indium (In) is used in smart phones. At current usage rates, indium will be used up in 50 years. Suggest one way humans could contribute to sustaining levels of this element for future generations.

Recycle. (3)

(f) Aluminium reacts with chlorine to form the compound aluminium chloride. Use the Periodic Table on page 79 of the *Formulae and Tables* booklet to predict the ratio of aluminium to chlorine in this compound. Hence write the chemical formula for aluminium chloride.

Aluminium in group 3. (3)

Chlorine in group 7. (3)

Al : Cl is 1 : 3. (3)

AlCl. (3)

(g) Elements can be classified as metals or non-metals.

The table shows some of the properties of three elements from the Periodic Table.

	Melting point (°C)	Boiling point (°C)	Conductor of electricity
Element 1	1538	2862	Yes
Element 2	−7	59	No
Element 3	−101	−34	No

(i) Which element (**1**, **2**, or **3**) is most likely to be a metal? Justify your answer.
1: conducts electricity. (3 × 2)

(ii) Which element (**1**, **2**, or **3**) is a liquid at room temperature (20 °C)? Justify your answer.
2: melting point below room temperature, boiling point above room temp. (3 × 3)

Sample Questions

Section A

1. Use the Periodic Table to answer the following questions:

(a) How many electrons are in the outer shell of group 2?
Two.

(b) The rows on a Periodic Table are called periods. How many energy levels are in the atoms of each element in period 2 (Li–Ne)?
Two.

(c) What is the group number of the halogens?
Seven.

(d) What do the elements in each group have in common?
Same number of electrons in their outer shell and so will have the same chemical reactivity.

2. Write the chemical formulae for the compounds formed by the following combinations of elements:

(a) Potassium and oxygen.
K_2O.

(b) Carbon and oxygen.
CO_2.

Section B

1. Katie received an email offering her the chance to buy sodium that had been collected from a riverbed. How did Katie know that the email was spam?
There would not be much if any sodium in a riverbed.

2. Explain the science behind this joke: Helium walks into a cafe. The waiter says, 'I am sorry, we don't serve noble gases.' Helium doesn't react.
Noble gases do not react as they are already stable (full outer shell).

29 Chemical Reactions

 Learning Outcomes

7. Investigate the effect of a number of variables on the rate of chemical reactions, including the production of common gases and biochemical reactions.

9. Consider chemical reactions in terms of energy, using the terms exothermic, endothermic and activation energy, and use simple energy profile diagrams to illustrate energy changes.

 aims By the end of this chapter you should:
- understand the production of gases in chemical reactions
- be able to classify exothermic and endothermic reactions
- be able to illustrate energy changes
- know the factors that affect the rate of reactions

The rate of a chemical reaction is the change in concentration of any one reactant or product per unit time.

- When we measure the rate of a chemical reaction we are measuring how much of any one material is either used up or made **per second (s^{-1})**

$$\text{Rate} = \frac{1}{\text{Time (s)}}$$

key point

A chemical reaction happens when the elements in a set of materials break apart and/or join together to form a different set of materials.

Production of Common Gases

Production of oxygen

- Oxygen can be produced in the laboratory by breaking down hydrogen peroxide.

$$2H_2O_2 \rightarrow 2H_2O + O_2$$

- A catalyst can be added to make the reaction go faster.

A **catalyst** is a substance that speeds up a chemical reaction by lowering the activation energy required. The catalyst does not get used up in the reaction itself.

- Manganese dioxide or iron chloride are two chemicals that act as a catalyst for the breakdown of hydrogen peroxide.

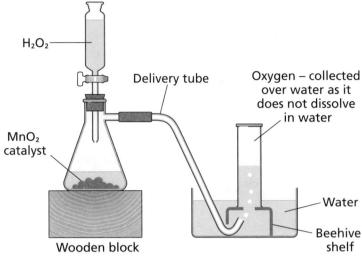

Manganese dioxide used as a catalyst to break down hydrogen peroxide into water and oxygen

Production of carbon dioxide

Carbon dioxide is produced by chemical reactions between acids and carbonates.

> Acid + Carbonate ➡ Salt + Water + Carbon Dioxide

Baking soda and marble chips are both made from carbonates.

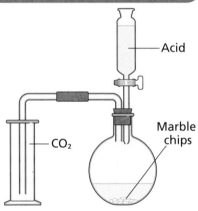

Adding acid to marble chips to produce carbon dioxide

Energy and Chemical Reactions

Exothermic reactions give out energy as heat.

- Occur when the reactants require more energy to stay together than the products, and the extra energy used on forming the products is released as heat.

Endothermic reactions take in energy as heat.

- Occur when the product requires more energy to stay together than the reactants, and energy must be taken in from the surroundings.

Know the differences between exothermic and endothermic reactions.

- Results in the surroundings becoming colder.

> Endothermic: **A + B + Heat → C**   ΔH=+≠
>
> Exothermic: **A + B → C + Heat**   ΔH=−≠

For a reaction to occur, the reacting particles must collide. A collision will only result in the formation of products if a certain minimum energy is reached.

Activation energy is the minimum energy needed for a reaction to take place.

Energy profile diagrams are a way of representing the energy changes in a chemical reaction on a graph.

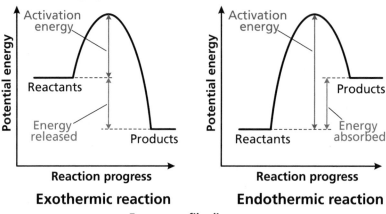

Energy profile diagrams

Biochemical Reactions

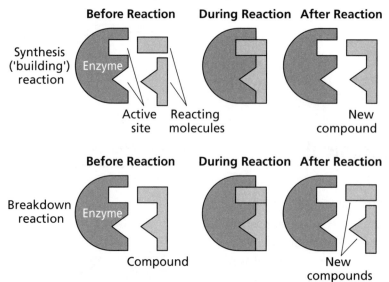

Biochemical reactions involving enzymes

Biochemical reactions are the chemical reactions that take place inside living things.

- Cause food to be broken down.
- Release energy from food.

- Help calcium strengthen bones.
- Allow plants to make food and oxygen.

Enzymes are biological catalysts made of protein.

- They control all biological reactions in our bodies.
- Similar to catalysts, they do not get used up in a reaction.
- **Denaturing** is when the temperature gets too high and enzymes change shape, making them unable to bond with reactants.
- Enzymes also work best at particular pH levels. **Buffer solutions** can be used to maintain this optimum pH level.

Factors Affecting Rate of Reactions

1. **Particle size** – smaller particles react faster.
   - If the collisions between particles during a reaction have enough energy, the particles react and new products are formed.
   - Once the outer particles have reacted, then the inner particles move to the surface and start to collide.
   - When particle sizes are smaller, then there is more material on the surface available to react, speeding up the process.

2. **Concentration** – increasing the concentration of a solution increases the rate of reaction because it means that there are more particles per unit volume of a solution to react.
   - Creates a higher number of colliding particles.

3. **Temperature** – increasing temperature increases the rate of reaction as it gives particles more energy.
   - The more energy the particles have, the faster they move and the more collisions between particles there will be.

4. **Catalysts** – speed up rate of reaction as they make it easier for particles to react.

Sample Questions

Section A

1. Draw a chart of the results you would expect from an experiment to measure the effect of particle size on the time taken for a reaction.

   Increasing surface area increases the rate of reaction.

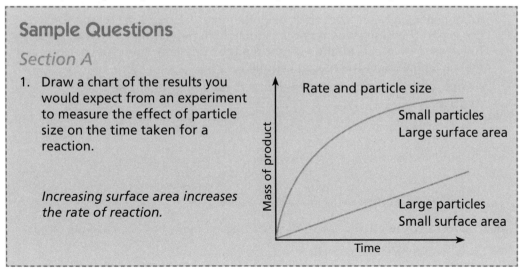

2. Draw an energy profile diagram for an exothermic reaction. In this diagram include:
    (a) the reactants.
    (b) the products.
    (c) the activation energy.
    (d) the energy change during the reaction.

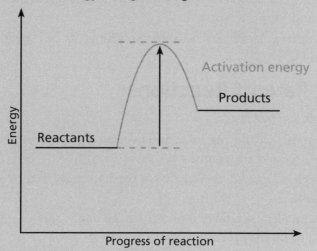

Section B

1. Biological washing powders contain enzymes to break down grease on clothes. Manufacturers advertise these as being energy saving washing powders because they work at lower temperatures. What do you think would be the ideal temperature to wash clothes at with a biological washing powder? What would happen if you used one of these washing powders on a very hot (90 °C) wash?

    Ideal temperature 30–40 °C. At 90 °C, the enzymes would become denatured, losing their function.

2. When a person has a fever their body temperature rises. The reason for this is that the higher temperature should help defeat invading infections. However, this affects all the reactions in the body and causes the person to feel unwell. Explain the reason for this.

    At this new temperature enzymes aren't reacting at their optimum (best) rate.

 **Learning Outcome**

10. Evaluate how humans contribute to sustainability through the extraction, use, disposal and recycling of materials.

 By the end of this chapter you should:
- familiarise yourself with the materials extracted by humans and consider the effects these processes have
- evaluate the recycling of materials

Extraction

Before materials are processed and converted into useful forms they are called **raw materials**.

- Most extraction methods leave a significant impact on the environment.

1. Wood

Clear cutting – involves cutting all trees from an area using heavy machinery.

Effects of Deforestation
Loss of biodiversity – *Forests are home to over 70% of animals, plants and other organisms.*
Food insecurity – *1.6 billion people living in poverty depend on forests for their food, fuel and livelihoods.*
Loss of natural resources – *Flooding and soil erosion result from deforestation.*
Global warming – *20% of global CO_2 emissions are caused by deforestation.*

Selective logging – only certain trees are removed, which helps biodiversity and reduces damage to the environment.

2. Metals

Metals come from ores, which have to be mined.

- Mining is heavily mechanised and carefully monitored in some countries.
- But in some countries mining is less controlled, with unsafe work conditions.

Societal impact refers to how something impacts a community of people.

Societal impacts of mining:

- Forced relocation of local people.
- Conflict for control over areas rich in valuable metals.
- Large amounts of earth and water are moved, which can release toxins and chemicals into the environment.

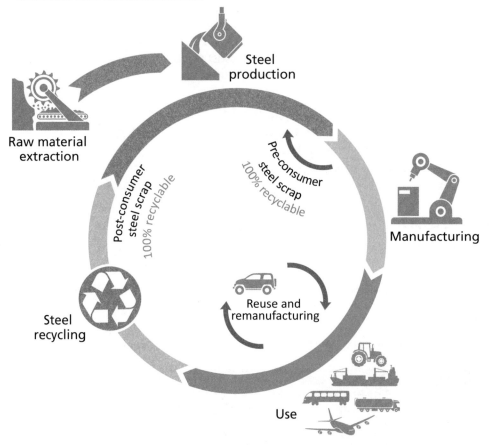

Steel life cycle

3. Plastics

Plastics are produced from crude oil. They are long lasting, easy to mould and suitable for many uses. The risks are as follows:

- Oil spills during the extraction and transport of oil.
- They are not usually biodegradable.

Processing Materials

Processes carried out to convert raw materials to useful products require large amounts of energy and chemicals.

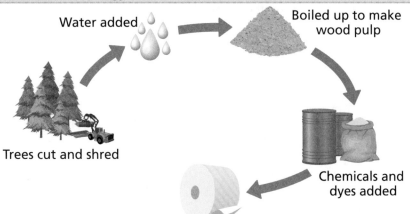

Water added

Boiled up to make wood pulp

Trees cut and shred

Chemicals and dyes added

Pulp poured over fine mesh and squeezed between rollers

Processing tress to make paper

Disposal of Materials

Reducing Waste Generation → Recycling → Waste Incineration

Recycling materials

The lifespans of some common materials are outlined below:

Material	Lifespan
Paper towels	2–4 weeks
Newspapers	6 weeks
Cotton	1–5 months
Tin cans	Approx. 50 years
Aluminium cans	200 years
Plastic bottles	70–450 years
Fishing line	600 years
Glass bottles	1–2 million years

Why recycle?

- Recycling reduces the extraction of raw materials.
- Recycling saves energy as less is needed to recycle materials compared with obtaining and refining them for their raw form.
- Recycling reduces the amount of waste that is released into the environment.

key point

If materials are not recycled, they are left to break down, either in landfills or elsewhere in the environment.

Sample Questions

Section A

1. Packaging is unavoidable but many products use excess packaging, for example Easter eggs and food products that are individually wrapped. Give three actions that you can take to reduce the amount of packaging you use.

   Choose reusable products.
   Buy in bulk.
   Take own bags shopping.

2. Waste can cause a lot of harm to the environment. List five ways in which waste can harm plants, animals, and the environment.

   Animals can ingest plastic and die.
   Toxic chemicals can harm plants and animals.
   Air pollution can cause acid rain.
   Polluted rivers kill fish from depleted oxygen.

3. 'Reduce, reuse, recycle' is a slogan that is used to encourage people to reduce their impact on the environment. Explain how this approach can achieve this.

   It is simple, memorable and tells individuals what they can do.

Section B

1. Explain why charities look for people's old mobile phones. In your answer refer to the materials that are used to manufacture mobile phones.

   Charities can recycle the harmful materials in mobile phones, making money and preventing them from getting into the environment where they would cause damage, e.g. mercury and lead.

Physical World

Contents

31 Measurements and Units

→ **Learning Outcome**

1. Select and use appropriate measuring instruments.

aims By the end of this chapter you should:
- be able to calculate and apply correct measurements and units
- appreciate the importance of measurements and units in science

The International System of Units

The SI system is a standard system of measurement used around the world that makes it easier for scientists to share and compare their results.

Measurement	SI Unit
Length	Metre
Mass	Kilogram
Time	Second
Temperature	Kelvin

Length

- Length is a measurement of distance between two points along a straight or curved line.
- SI unit: metres (m).
- Other units: centimetres (cm) and kilometres (km).

Instruments to measure length:

1. **Metre stick** – straight lines.
2. **Opisometer** – short, curved lines.
3. **Digital map measurer** – short, curved lines.
4. **Trundle wheel** – long, curved lengths.
5. **Vernier callipers** – diameters or widths of solid objects.

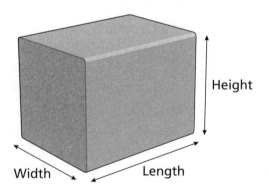

Height

Width   Length

Note on zero error

- The scale on some metre sticks and rulers does not start at zero.
- If this is not taken into account, it can lead to inaccuracies in measurements. This is called zero error.

Mass

- Mass is a measure of how much matter something contains.
- SI unit: kilograms (kg).
- Other units: grams (g).

Time

- SI unit: seconds (s).
- Stopwatches can be used to accurately tell how much time has passed.
- The most accurate clocks in the world are atomic clocks.

Temperature

- Temperature is a measure of how hot something is.
- SI unit: Kelvin (K).
- Other units: Celsius, Fahrenheit.
- Scientists use the Kelvin scale as it does not use negative numbers.
- Absolute zero = 0 K. This is the coldest anything can be and equals $-273.15\,°C$ on the Celsius scale.
- Temperature is measured with a thermometer.

Area

- Area is the measure of the size of the surface of an object, using measurements of length.
- Common units = km^2, m^2, cm^2, mm^2.
- Land is measured in hectares; one hectare = 10,000 m^2.

Rectangles and squares = length × width.

Irregularly shaped objects = trace the outline of the object onto squared graph paper and count the squares; one square = 1 cm^2.

Surface area of a cube = area of each side added together = 6 × (length × length).

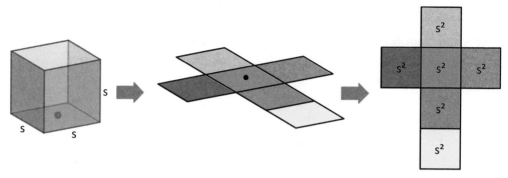

Surface area of cube with sides, s = 6s²

Volume

- Volume is the measure of how much space something takes up.
- Common units = m^3, cm^3, mm^3.

Regularly shaped box = length × width × height.

Liquids = pour the liquid into a graduated cylinder and read the volume.

Irregularly shaped objects = use a graduated cylinder (see how much the water rises), or an overflow can (see how much water is pushed from the can).

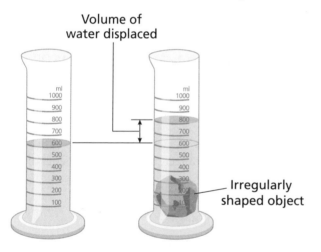

Measuring the volume of an irregularly shaped object using a graduated cylinder

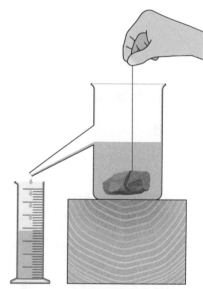

Measuring the volume of an irregularly shaped object using an overflow can

Meniscus

The surface at the top of a liquid is curved. The curved surface of the liquid is called the meniscus. When we read a volume of a liquid in a container, we take the reading at the bottom of the meniscus.

Graduated cylinder

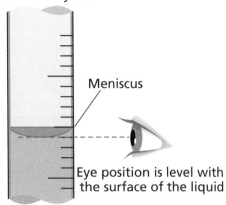

Meniscus

Eye position is level with the surface of the liquid

(The unit of measurement is millilitre)

Reading a volume of liquid

Accuracy and Precision

Average reading: When scientists take more than one measurement of the same thing, but not all the results are equal. In these cases, an average value can be calculated from the results.

$$\text{Average} \quad = \quad \frac{\text{Sum of Measurements}}{\text{Number of Measurements}}$$

Choosing the right instruments to use depends on the accuracy and precision of the instruments.

Example: Digital callipers are more accurate than a tape measure, but only measure distances of 10 or 20 cm.

Digital callipers

Example: Laboratory pipettes are used to measure small volumes of liquid, but they can only measure a fixed volume such as 15 cm^3.

Example: A 100 cm^3 measuring cylinder is less accurate when measuring the volume of a liquid, but can hold bigger quantities.

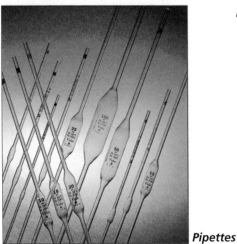

Pipettes

exam
Q

Exam Paper 2019

Question 2

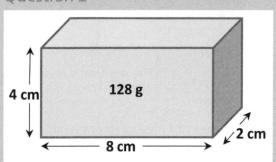

4 cm

128 g

8 cm

2 cm

A student was asked to measure the density of a block.

The dimensions of the block are shown in the diagram.

The mass of the block is 128 g.

(a) Calculate the volume of the block.

   4 × 8 × 2 = 64 cm³. (3)

(b) Calculate the density of the block. Include the unit for your answer.

   $$Density = \frac{Mass}{Volume}$$

   $\frac{128}{64}$ *= 2 g/cm³.* (2 × 3)

(c) The photograph below shows three glasses of water labelled **A**, **B** and **C**. An egg was placed into each glass. The photograph was taken when the eggs were stationary.

Which glass (**A**, **B** or **C**) contains the egg with the greatest density?

Give a reason for your answer.

C – It is the egg that sinks the most, i.e. has the greatest density. (2 × 3)

Sample Paper 2019

Question 2

Complete the table below for the instruments shown.

In each case, state what physical quantity the instrument measures.

Also state the unit used for that measurement.

(Some parts of the table are already completed for you.)

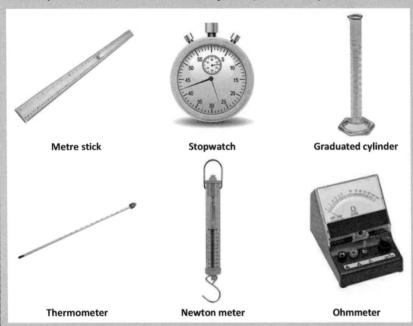

| Metre stick | Stopwatch | Graduated cylinder |

| Thermometer | Newton meter | Ohmmeter |

Instrument	Quantity Measured	Unit
Metre Stick	*Length*	*Metre*
Stopwatch	*Time*	*Second*
Graduated Cylinder	*Volume*	*cm³*
Thermometer	*Temperature*	*Celsius*
Newton Meter	*Force*	*Newton*
Ohmmeter	Resistance	Ohm

Sample Questions

Section A

1. Calculate the area of a rectangle of length 7 cm and width 9 cm.

    7 × 9 = 63 m² (area = length × width).

2. How would you calculate the area of a leaf?

    *Lay the leaf to be measured on a 1 cm grid and trace the outline.
    Count the number of square centimetres. Estimate the area of the partial
    squares.*

3. Calculate the volume of a large box of length 2 m, width 3 m and height 9 m.

    2 × 3 × 9 = 54 m³ (length × width × height).

4. The level of water in a graduated cylinder increases from 26 cm³ to 53 cm³
    when a stone is placed in it. What is the volume of the stone?

    53 – 26 = 27 cm³.

5. Calculate the surface area of a cube with a length that equals 3 cm.

    All sides the same; 3 × 3 × 3 = 27 cm³.

Section B

1. Describe how an overflow can is used to measure the volume of a small
    stone.

    *Drop the stone into a graduated cylinder containing water and note the
    new volume.
    To get the volume of the stone, subtract the two readings.*

2. How would you measure the volume of a cork using an overflow can?

    *It is possible to measure the volume of naturally floating objects. By using a
    sinker (an object designed to sink the body) of known volume to immerse the
    floating object, we can calculate the volume of the floating object. Measure
    the volume of water displaced and subtract the volume of the sinker.*

3. How do you correctly measure the volume of a liquid in a graduated
    cylinder?

    *Place the graduated cylinder on a flat surface and view the height of the
    liquid in the cylinder with your eyes directly level with the liquid. The liquid
    will tend to curve downward. This curve is called the meniscus. Always read
    the measurement at the bottom of the meniscus.*

32 Density, Speed, Acceleration

32 Density, Speed, Acceleration

 Learning Outcome

2. Identify and measure/calculate length, mass, time, temperature, area, volume, density, speed, acceleration, force, potential difference, current, resistance, electrical power.

aims By the end of this chapter you should:
- develop the use of units to apply to other areas
- explore the scientific effects of these units

Density

- Density is the mass per unit volume of a substance, i.e. the relationship between its mass and the amount of space it takes up.
- Units = g/cm^3 = $g\,cm^{-3}$.

$$\text{Density} = \frac{\text{Mass}}{\text{Volume}}$$

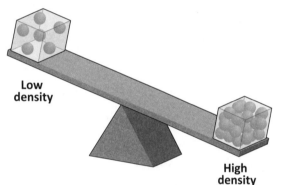

Low density

High density

Two objects with equal volumes but different densities

NOTE:
The density of a particular substance is always the same, even if we use different volumes of that substance to do our calculations. Density is a characteristic property of a substance and does not change.

exam focus

Be aware of why objects float and how water's unique properties are key in our explanation.

- When water freezes, the molecules in it move further apart from each other.
- Therefore, the frozen water takes up more space.
- The ice still has the same mass as when it was water, but the volume has now increased.
- Therefore, its density is now less than water.

key point

An object floats because its density is less than the density of the liquid it is in.

Speed

- Speed is the distance travelled per unit time.
- Units = m/s = m s^{-1}.

$$\text{Speed} \quad = \quad \frac{\text{Distance}}{\text{Time}}$$

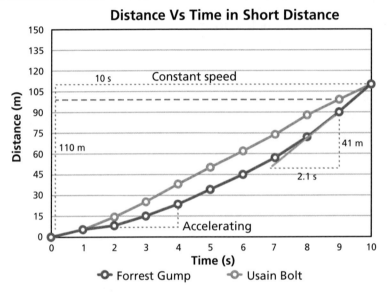

Distance Vs Time in Short Distance

Forrest Gump   Usain Bolt

Above is a graph representing the distance vs time for the two greatest sprinters in human history, Forrest Gump and Usain Bolt. From this graph we can see the relationship between distance and time for the two athletes, as well as calculate their speed at any given moment in the race.

Velocity is the speed of an object in a particular direction.

- **Example:** If a car travels at a speed of 60 km/h from Dublin to Wexford, its velocity = 60 km/h due south.

Acceleration

- Acceleration is the change in velocity per unit time; it is always the result of a force.
- Unit = m/s^2.
- You can always feel this force causing acceleration.
- **Example:** As a plane takes off, it is accelerating, and passengers can feel this sensation. However, as the plane cruises at high altitudes, the passengers cannot feel it, even though it is still moving very fast.
- Deceleration is the opposite of acceleration.

$$\text{Acceleration} \quad = \quad \frac{\text{Change in Velocity}}{\text{Time Taken}}$$

Speed vs time graph

On the right is a speed vs time graph for Olympian athlete Usain Bolt.

If we want to find out Bolt's acceleration between 2 seconds and 4 seconds, we can use the formula above.

Speed after 2 seconds = 9.75 m/s

Speed after 4 seconds = 11.75 m/s

Time taken = 2 seconds

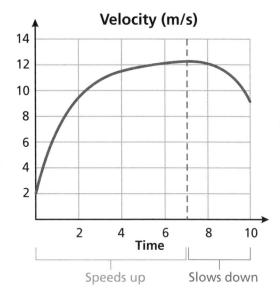

Velocity (m/s)

Speeds up   Slows down

Therefore,

$$\text{Acceleration} = \frac{\text{Change in Velocity}}{\text{Time Taken}} = \frac{(11.75 - 9.75)}{2} = 1 \text{ m/s}^2$$

exam Q

Exam Paper 2019

Question 7

The graph below represents the journey of a cyclist.

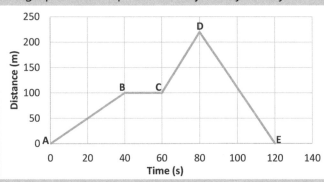

(a) Name an instrument that could be used to measure the time taken for the journey.
   Stopwatch. (3)

(b) Calculate the average speed of the cyclist as he travelled from point **A** to point **B**.
   $$Speed = \frac{Distance}{Time} \quad : \quad \frac{100}{40} = 2.5 \text{ m/s. } (3)$$

(c) Describe the cyclist's motion between points **B** and **C** of his journey.
   Stopped (flat line means distance has not changed). (3)

(d) The cyclist's speed as he travelled from point **A** to point **B** was less than his speed as he travelled from point C to point **D**. What evidence is there in the graph to support this?

The line from A – B has a smaller slope (less steep).
*note steeper slope means greater speed. (3)

(e) Describe what the cyclist did at point **D**.
Travelled back to his original point. (3)

Sample Questions

Section A

1. Air expands when it is heated. Use this observation to explain how a hot air balloon works.

   By heating the air inside the balloon it becomes lighter. This lighter air rises, causing the balloon to float upwards.

2. What is the density of a block of wood of volume 200 cm^3 and mass 180 g?

   $$Density = \frac{Mass}{Volume}$$

   $$Density = \frac{180}{200} = 0.9 \ g/cm^3.$$

3. What is the difference between speed and acceleration?

   Speed is the distance travelled per unit time.
   Acceleration is the change in speed (or velocity) per unit time.

4. (a) A car travels 200 m in 8 s. What is its average speed?

   $$Speed = \frac{Distance}{Time}$$

   $$Speed = \frac{200}{8} = 25 \ m/s.$$

   (b) A car increases its velocity from 15 m/s to 25 m/s in 7 s. Calculate its acceleration.

   $$Acceleration = \frac{Change\ in\ Velocity}{Time\ Taken}$$

   $$Acceleration = \frac{(25 - 15)}{7} = 1.4286 \ m/s^2.$$

   (c) A car starts from rest with a constant acceleration of 6 m/s^2. How long will it take it to reach a speed of 30 m/s?

   $$Time = \frac{Change\ in\ Velocity}{Acceleration}$$

   $$Time = \frac{(30 - 0)}{6} = 5 \ seconds \quad *started\ from\ rest = 0\ m/s.$$

Section B

1. This graph shows the distances travelled at different times by a boy running.

Time (s)	0	1	2	3	4	5	6	7	8
Distance (m)	0	4	8	12	16	20	24	28	32

Graph the results, putting time on the horizontal axis.

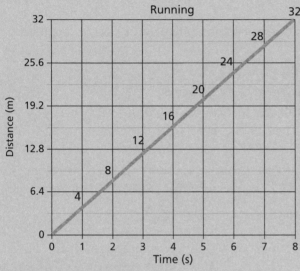

Use the graph to find:

(a) The time taken to run 10 m.

   2.5 seconds.

(b) The distance travelled in 5.5 seconds.

   22 m.

(c) The speed of the runner.

   $\dfrac{32}{8} = 4\ m/s.$

2. What does the shape of the graph tell you about the relationship between time and the distance the boy has run?

   Moving at a constant speed. They are both increasing linearly.

3. Sketch a similar graph to show the boy gradually slowing down as he runs.

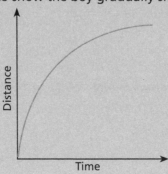

33 Force

Learning Outcome

3. Investigate patterns and relationships between physical observables.

 aims By the end of this chapter you should:
- be able to illustrate Newton's three laws
- know how to identify the effects of friction
- be able to explain the difference between weight and mass

A force is anything that causes an object to move or change velocity (speed or direction).

- SI unit: Newton (N).
- Named after Sir Isaac Newton.
- **Examples:** Push, pull, weight, friction.

 key point

Unless a force acts on it, an object at rest stays at rest, and an object in motion stays in motion with the same speed and in the same direction.

Newton's First Law

An object at rest will remain at rest

Unless acted on by an unbalanced force

An object in motion will continue with constant speed and direction

Unless acted on by an unbalanced force

Newton's First Law demonstrated with a football

Friction

Friction is a force that prevents easy movement between two objects that are in contact. Friction is affected by:

1. Downward force.
2. The roughness of a surface.

Smooth surfaces   Rough surfaces

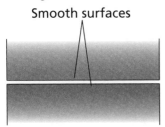 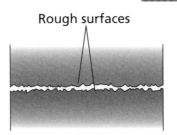

Friction force is affected by the smoothness of the surfaces

Advantages of Friction	Disadvantages of Friction
Allows good grip between car tyres and the road	Causes moving parts in an engine to wear away
Brakes in a car use friction to stop	Causes burns when climbing ropes
Warms hands when they are rubbed together	Friction with the air slows down vehicles, reducing fuel efficiency

Ways to reduce unwanted friction: Lubrication, make the surfaces smoother, etc.

Newton's Second Law

Force = Mass × Acceleration

When a force acts on a mass, it accelerates. The greater the force, the greater the acceleration.

Newton's Second Law in action as a human exerts force to accelerate another object

Weight

Weight is the force of gravity acting on an object.

- Not to be confused with mass.
- Weight is measured in Newtons.
- On the surface of the Earth, gravity pulls everything down with an acceleration of approximately 10 m/s².
- Because weight is a force, we can calculate it using the formula for Newton's second law:

  Example: My weight on Earth is around 560 N.

  My weight on the Moon is around 90 N.

  My mass is always 56 kg.

Weight = Mass × Acceleration due to gravity

Weight on the surface of the Earth = Mass × 10

Newton's Third Law

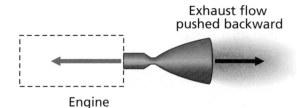

Exhaust flow
pushed backward

Engine
pushed forward

Rocket engine thrust

key point

For every action there is an equal and opposite reaction.

Example: When air is pushed out of a balloon, it causes the balloon to push forward in the opposite direction.

Sample Questions

Section A

1. How does mass affect the force needed to move an object?

   More mass, more force needed.

2. Determine the force when an object of mass 3 kg is given an acceleration of 2 m/s².

   Force = Mass × Acceleration.
   Force = 3 × 2 = 6 N.

3. A force of 15 N is exerted on an object to cause it to accelerate at a rate of 5 m/s^2. Determine the mass of the object.

$$Mass = \frac{Force}{Acceleration}$$

$$Mass = \frac{15}{5} = 3 \ kg.$$

Section B

1. Suppose that a 10 kg skateboard is accelerating at a rate of 2 m/s^2. If the force is tripled and the mass is doubled, then what is the new acceleration of the skateboard?

   Original force = 10 × 2 = 20 N.

   New force = 20 × 3 = 60 N.

   New mass = 10 × 2 = 20 kg.

   New acceleration = 3 m/s^2.

2. Which law of motion explains:
   (a) Why a ball eventually stops moving after it is kicked?
   Newton's Third Law: For every action there is an equal and opposite reaction.
   Air and grass pushing against the ball.
   (b) Why we need to wear seatbelts?
   Newton's First Law: Unless a force acts on it, an object at rest stays at rest, and an object in motion stays in motion with the same speed and in the same direction.
   Without seatbelts in an accident, a person's body would keep travelling.
   (c) How rockets are launched into space?
   Newton's Third Law: For every action there is an equal and opposite reaction.
   When rocket fuel is burned and pushed out the bottom of the rocket, the ground pushes back with an equal amount of force launching the rocket into space.
   (d) Why a 50 kg bag on Earth weighs more than a 50 kg bag in space?
   Newton's Second Law: When a force acts on a mass, it accelerates. The greater the force, the greater the acceleration.
   Greater force of gravity on Earth.

3. Describe one way to show that every force has an equal but opposite force.

   Blow up but do not tie a balloon. When air is pushed out of a balloon it causes the balloon to push forward in the opposite direction.

4. Explain how a spring balance works.

   A spring balance is a spring fixed at one end with a hook to attach an object at the other. By figuring out the distance that the spring moves it is possible to calculate the force exerted by the object.

5. Give a reason for the following:

(a) A car has broken down. The driver must ask for help to push it.
Driver cannot exert a force greater than the car by themselves.

(b) Trolleys are used to move heavy furniture.
Wheels change the amount of force needed for a load.

(c) Buses need more powerful engines than cars.
Buses are heavier than cars and so need more force to move them.

(d) Accelerating quickly in a car uses more fuel than accelerating slowly.
More force needed.

(e) It is more difficult for a runner to increase his/her speed than to run at a constant speed.
Expending more energy to produce more of a force for acceleration.

34 Energy

Learning Outcomes

6. Explain energy conservation and analyse processes in terms of energy changes and dissipation.

7. Design, build and test a device that transforms energy from one form to another in order to perform a function; describe the energy changes and ways of improving efficiency.

aims By the end of this chapter you should:
- know how to describe energy and its different types
- appreciate the law of conservation of energy and consider it in terms of dissipation of energy
- discuss energy efficiency, conservation and their use in the home

- There are many different forms of energy (e.g. heat and light).
- Energy can change from one form or another and can be transferred from one object to another but cannot be created or destroyed.
- SI unit: joule (J).

key point

ENERGY is the ability to do work.

The Sun

The Sun is the primary source of energy on Earth.

- It provides us with light and heat energy.
- Nearly all other forms of energy are produced from the Sun, directly or indirectly.
- Photosynthesis is reliant on the Sun's energy.
- Plants are eaten and then this energy is released during respiration.

exam focus

Explain the importance of the Sun to life on Earth.

Types of Energy

1. **Potential energy:** Stored energy.
2. **Kinetic energy:** The energy of movement.

Energy	
Potential	**Kinetic**
Examples:	**Examples:**
● Chemical	● Electrical
● Gravitational	● Sound
● Elastic	● Light
● Nuclear	● Wind
	● Thermal

The Law of Conservation of Energy

The total amount of energy in the universe has neither increased nor decreased since the time of the Big Bang.

Examples of Energy Changes

Energy transformation is when one type of energy changes to another type of energy.

Torch

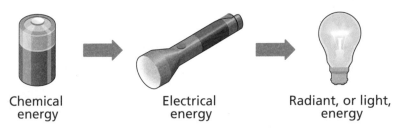

| Chemical energy | Electrical energy | Radiant, or light, energy |

Energy changes in a torch

Energy Input	Energy Output 1	Energy Output 2
Chemical energy	Electrical energy	Light energy

Television

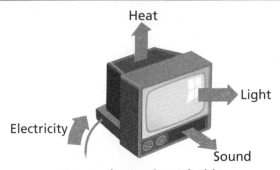

Heat

Light

Electricity

Sound

Energy changes in a television

Energy Input	Energy Output
Electrical energy	Light energy + sound energy + heat energy

Wind turbine

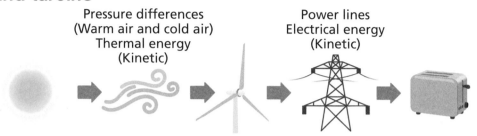

Pressure differences
(Warm air and cold air)
Thermal energy
(Kinetic)

Power lines
Electrical energy
(Kinetic)

Sun
Radiant energy
(Kinetic)

Wind turbine
Mechanical energy
(Kinetic)

Toaster
Thermal energy
(Kinetic)

Energy changes in a wind turbine

Energy Input	Energy Output
Motion energy	Electrical energy

Sling shot

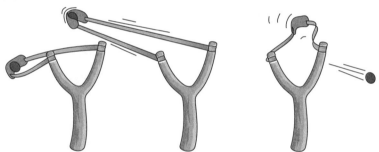

Energy changes in a sling shot

Energy Input	Energy Output
Elastic potential energy	Motion energy

Energy Transfer and Dissipation

Energy dissipation: Energy that escapes and spreads out into the surrounding area during an energy transfer.

- This occurs because some energy is useful to the transfer while some is not.

Example 1: A moving snooker ball

1. Motion energy in the cue is transferred to the ball, causing it to move.

2. Some of the motion energy is converted to sound energy.

3. The motion energy in the ball decreases until it comes to a stop.

4. This is due to the motion energy being dissipated by the friction between the ball and the table.

5. Friction causes the motion energy to be dissipated into heat energy.

Example 2: A swinging pendulum

1. Downswing – gravitational energy converted to motion energy.
2. Upswing – motion energy converted to gravitational potential energy.
3. Some motion energy is dissipated as heat energy into the air.
4. Causes height of each swing to become lower and lower.

Energy Efficiency

Sankey diagram: Shows how much energy is changed into useful forms, and into forms that are not useful and which dissipate.

- The thicker the arrow in the diagram then the greater the amount of energy involved.

Filament light bulb

Input: Electrical energy 100 J → Output: Light energy 10 J, heat energy 90 J

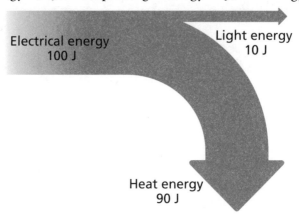

Modern energy-saving bulb

Input: Electrical energy 100 J → Output: Light energy 75 J, heat energy 25 J

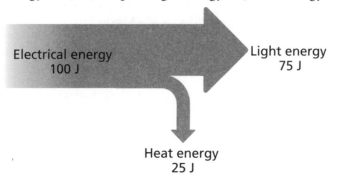

$$\text{Efficiency} \quad = \quad \frac{\text{Useful Energy Output}}{\text{Total Energy Input}} \quad = \quad \text{\% Efficiency}$$

Improving Energy Efficiency

Energy is often wasted due to friction and heat loss. It is possible to improve the efficiency of an object by reducing the amount of friction or energy lost as heat.

Reducing friction: Adding oil as a lubricant improves the efficiency of an engine.

Reducing heat loss: Covering a hot water tank with a lagging jacket reduces the heat loss.

Energy Conservation in the Home

Building Energy Rating (BER): New houses being sold or leased must have a BER certificate, which tells us the energy efficiency of a house, i.e. how much energy is needed to heat and light it.

Most efficient

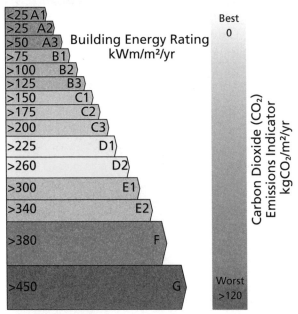

Least efficient

How to improve the energy efficiency of your home:

- Insulate the hot water tank.
- Insulate the walls/attic/floor.
- Install double glazed windows/doors.
- Replace old boilers.
- Install a heating thermostat.
- Install renewable energy heating systems.
- Use energy efficient appliances.

Exam Paper 2019

Question 13

Electrical energy is one of the most important types of energy that we use in our daily lives.

An electrical appliance has a power rating which tells you how much electricity it uses.

The table below shows the power rating of some common household appliances and the forms of energy that are produced in the appliances.

Appliance	Power rating (W)	Forms of energy produced	Current used (A)
Coffee maker	1380	Heat, Sound	6
Television	115	Heat, Light, Sound	0.5
Kitchen blender	345	Heat, Kinetic, Sound	1.5
Dishwasher	2300	Heat, Kinetic, Sound	10

(a) Which appliance listed in the table uses the most electrical energy?

Dishwasher. (3)

(b) (i) Select one of the appliances from the table above and name a useful form of energy produced when the appliance is being used.

Name of appliance: Kitchen blender.

Useful form of energy: Kinetic. (3)

(ii) For the appliance you have selected, name an unwanted form of energy produced.

Heat. (3)

(iii) For the appliance you have selected, calculate the voltage applied across the appliance. Include the unit for your answer.

$$Voltage \ = \ \frac{Power \ (W)}{Current \ (I)}$$

$$= \ \frac{345}{1.5} \ = \ 230 \ V.$$ (2 × 3)

(c) What pattern, if any, exists between the power rating of the appliance and the current used?

Power is proportional to current. (3)

Sustainability issues arise from the generation and consumption of electricity.

(d) What do you understand by the term sustainability?

Sustainability is the use of a resource in such quantities so that it does not run out. (6)

(e) Suggest one way in which we can reduce how much electrical energy we use.

Turn off lights in rooms when we are not in them. (2)

(f) Electrical energy can be produced using renewable and non-renewable sources. Identify **two** renewable sources of energy from the list below by placing a tick (✔) in each of the correct boxes. (2 × 2)

Oil ☐

Solar ✔

Natural gas ☐

Wind ✔

Sample Paper 2019

Question 12

Sankey diagrams are named after H. Riall Sankey, a Tipperary-born engineer, following his 1898 description of the energy efficiency of a steam engine.

Sankey diagrams show the flow of energy to and from a device.

In a Sankey diagram, the width of each arrow represents the energy named.

The Sankey diagrams for a filament lamp and a compact fluorescent lamp (CFL) are shown right.

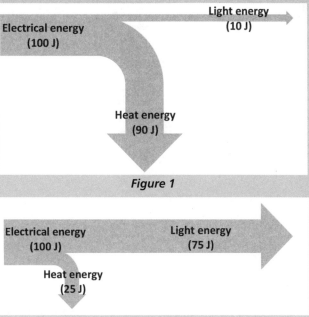

Light energy
(10 J)

Electrical energy
(100 J)

Heat energy
(90 J)

Figure 1

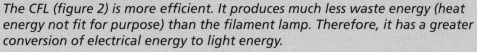

Electrical energy
(100 J)

Light energy
(75 J)

Heat energy
(25 J)

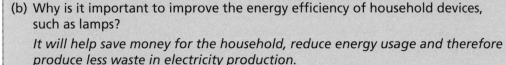

Figure 2

(a) Examine figures **1** and **2**. Which lamp is more efficient? Justify your answer.

The CFL (figure 2) is more efficient. It produces much less waste energy (heat energy not fit for purpose) than the filament lamp. Therefore, it has a greater conversion of electrical energy to light energy.

(b) Why is it important to improve the energy efficiency of household devices, such as lamps?

It will help save money for the household, reduce energy usage and therefore produce less waste in electricity production.

(c) A student is asked to investigate and compare the heat energy produced by filament lamps and CFLs.

Apart from the lamps themselves, name a piece of equipment that could be used during this investigation. Explain how this piece of equipment could be used during the investigation.

Thermometer – thermometers could be placed close to each bulb and the heat energy released may be measured and compared.

(d) The energy conversions that happen in a CFL are described in the table below.

Complete the table for another device which transforms energy from one form to another and which you designed as part of your studies in science.

Name of the device	Function of the device	Main useful energy conversion	Main loss of energy
Compact fluorescent lamp (CFL)	To provide artificial light	Electrical to light	Electrical to heat
Solar powered compactor	*Crush and compact waste in bins*	*Light to kinetic*	*Electrical to heat (friction)*

(e) Sketch a Sankey diagram for the device you described in part (d). Label each part of the diagram.

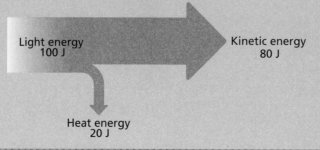

Light energy
100 J

Kinetic energy
80 J

Heat energy
20 J

Sample Questions

Section A

1. Explain how the Sun's energy is essential for each of these:
   (a) Plants
       Needed for photosynthesis for food.
   (b) Animals
       Need to eat the plants for energy.
   (c) Humans
       Need to eat the plants and animals.
   (d) Petrol
       Comes from dead plants and animals, which got their energy from photosynthesis.
   (e) Generation of electricity
       Produced the fossil fuels that make electricity.

2. Plants use energy from the Sun to make food during photosynthesis.
   (a) What form of energy is captured by the plant during photosynthesis?
       Light.
   (b) What form of energy is it changed into?
       Chemical.

3. A house has a building energy rating (BER) of A. List some of the possible features of this house that could contribute to its A rating.

   Solar panels for clean energy, double glazed windows/doors, insulated hot water tank.

Section B

1. A car engine makes noise and becomes hot when the car is running. Explain why. Use the following words in your explanation: energy, motion, heat, chemical, dissipation, sound.

   A car needs energy from petrol to run the engine. As motion begins, it produces waste heat and heat from friction. The chemical energy in the petrol allows this to occur. Some of the heat dissipates into the atmosphere and sound can be heard in movement.

2. A fridge has an energy efficiency rating of F. What does this tell you about the appliance?

   It is very inefficient. Appliances are rated from A+++ to G with G being the least efficient.

3. How can the efficiency of a device be improved?

   You could use more energy efficient light bulbs.

4. It is believed that a meteorite struck Earth 65 million years ago. Its impact caused dust particles to form a layer in the atmosphere, blocking out a lot of the Sun's energy. What effect do you think this had on life on Earth? Justify your answer.

   It would have put a stop to photosynthesis, blocking the source of all food on Earth.

5. Considering rollercoasters:
   (a) Which point has the most gravitational potential energy?
       The top, as it is at its highest and biggest stretch for gravity to act on it.
   (b) Which point has the most motion energy?
       The bottom, as it is no longer falling, just moving without gravitational force.
   (c) Do you think any of the motion energy is dissipated while the rollercoaster is running? Explain your answer.
       Yes, some is lost as heat. Due to friction with the track and air resistance.

 Learning Outcomes

6. Explain energy conservation and analyse processes in terms of energy changes and dissipation.

7. Design, build and test a device that transforms energy from one form to another in order to perform a function; describe the energy changes and ways of improving efficiency.

aims By the end of this chapter you should:
- develop an understanding of energy in terms of electricity
- appreciate the different electrical units and their interactions (Ohm's Law)
- develop this understanding into practical use in organising a functional electrical circuit

All matter is made of **atoms**, which contain **protons, neutrons** and **electrons.**

Charged atom: An atom is charged if there is a difference in the number of protons and electrons.

Static electricity: Generated when an atom becomes charged, e.g. small shock when you touch a car door after a journey.

Positive charge: An atom has a positive charge when there are fewer electrons than protons.

Negative charge: An atom has a negative charge when there are more electrons than protons.

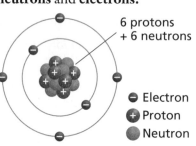

6 protons + 6 neutrons

● Electron
⊕ Proton
● Neutron

Carbon atom

Electric Discharge

The rapid transfer of electrons from one object to another.

Example: When you walk across a carpet your feet rub against it, pick up electrons and your body builds up an electric charge.

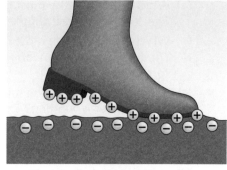

Electric discharge while walking on carpet

Voltage, Current and Power

Electrical power (P) is the rate at which electrical energy is either produced or consumed.
SI unit = watt (W)

> P = IV
>
> I = current (amps)
>
> V = voltage (volts)

Current Electricity

The flow of an electric charge through a conductor is called
current electricity.

Conductor: An object that allows an electric charge to flow
through it.

exam focus

Know the following
terms and symbols
by heart.

Electrical circuit: When a current flows in a closed loop or path.
- In order to flow through a circuit, electrons require a source of energy.
- Electrical energy is often supplied to electrical circuits by a cell or battery.

Electric potential: The ability to move electrons.

Potential difference/voltage (V): The difference between the electric
potential at two points in a circuit.
- SI unit: volts (V).
- Measured with a voltmeter.

Electric current (I): The
flow of electric charge.
- SI unit: amps (A).
- Measured with an ammeter.

Resistance (R): The opposition
to the flow of electrons in a circuit.
- Electrical resistance converts
electrical energy to other forms of
energy (i.e. heat or light).
- SI unit: ohms (Ω).
- Measured with an ohmmeter.

Voltmeter (left) and ammeter (right)

Ohmmeter

Designing and Building Electrical Circuits

Circuit diagrams: Represent electrical circuits, showing all the components of a circuit and how they connect to one another.

Series circuit: Only one path along which the electrons can flow.

Parallel circuit: More than one path along which electrons can flow.

Ammeter

Cell

Battery (2-cell)

Diode

Fuse

Lamp

Resistor

Resistor (variable)

LDR resistor (light dependent)

Switch (open)

Switch (closed)

Voltmeter

Symbols representing elements in electrical circuits

Series circuit

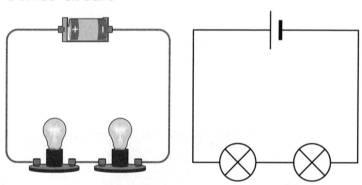

Circuit diagram (right) representing a series circuit

Parallel circuit

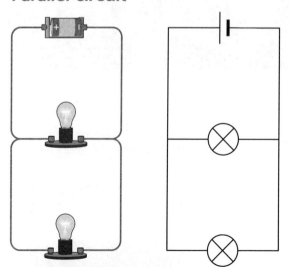

Circuit diagram (right) representing a parallel circuit

Ohm's Law

Georg Ohm (1789–1854).

- German scientist.
- Defined the relationship between voltage, current and resistance.
- This is known as **Ohm's Law**.

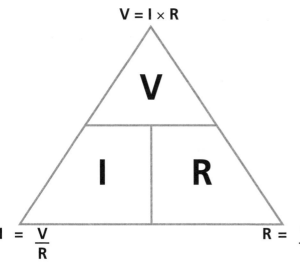

$$V = I \times R$$

$$I = \frac{V}{R} \qquad\qquad R = \frac{V}{I}$$

Ohm's Law Triangle can be used to calculate voltage, current and resistance

Georg Ohm

key point

OHM'S LAW

When the temperature is constant, the amount of steady current (I) passing through a material is directly proportional to the voltage across the material (V), so the greater the voltage, the greater the current.

Verifying Ohm's Law

Verification: When scientists carry out experiments to check a law is correct.
To verify Ohm's Law, set up a circuit like the one shown in the diagram below:

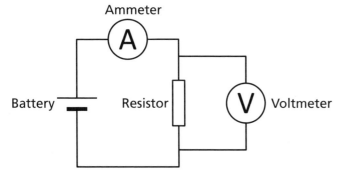

Circuit diagram of circuit with an ammeter and voltmeter

- When the voltage is increased on the circuit, it is found the current also increases.
- The resistance can be found by dividing any voltage value by its corresponding current value.
- The graph to the right illustrates the relationship between current and voltage.

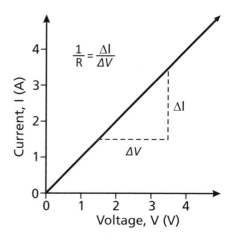

NOTE:
The voltmeter must always be connected in parallel.
- Because it measures the voltage between two points (usually before and after the resistor).
- An ohmmeter should also be connected in this way.

NOTE:
The ammeter must always be connected in series.
- As its purpose is to measure the current as it flows through the meter.

Effects of an Electric Current

- Heating effect, e.g. electric fires.
- Magnetic effect, e.g. an electromagnet in a loudspeaker.
- Chemical effect, e.g. it is used to separate water into hydrogen and oxygen in a process called electrolysis. This can be used to refine or purify metals.

Sample Paper 2019

Question 9

A student investigated the relationship between the potential difference (voltage) across a resistor and the current flowing through it.

The circuit diagram to the right shows the arrangement of the apparatus used by the student.

Examine the circuit diagram and answer the questions below.

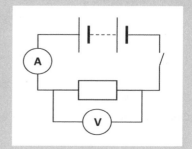

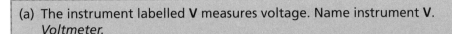

(a) The instrument labelled **V** measures voltage. Name instrument **V**.
   Voltmeter.

(b) The instrument labelled **A** measures current. Name instrument **A**.
   Ammeter.

(c) In the circuit diagram above, draw a circle around the symbol for the switch.
   Circle at open line on right side.

(d) The student found that current is proportional
   to voltage for this resistor.
   Using the axes provided, draw a sketch of a
   graph to show this relationship.

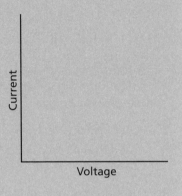

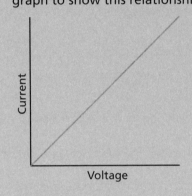

Sample Questions

Section A

1. Explain how objects can become charged.
   When they lose or gain an electron to become an ion.

2. What happens when two things with the same type of charge are brought
   into close contact?
   They repel each other.

3. Describe the relationship between potential difference and current in an
   electric circuit.
   The current (potential difference) is directly proportional to the voltage.

4. If a voltage of 8 volts gives a current of 2 amps across a resistor, what is the
   resistance of the resistor?

   $$Resistance = \frac{Voltage}{Current}$$

   $$Resistance = \frac{8}{2} = 4 \text{ ohms.}$$

5. What current will a circuit with a voltage of 6 volts give if it contains a 3 ohm resistor?

$$Current = \frac{Voltage}{Resistance}$$

$$Current = \frac{6}{2} = 3\ amps.$$

Section B

1. What causes lightning?

    When particles in the atmosphere bump into each other, electricity builds up. Lightning is really electricity. When the clouds get full of electricity from the collision of the ice and water particles, the electricity moves from the cloud to the ground below, or to another cloud.

2. How does an electrical switch control a circuit?

    A switch is a component that controls whether an electrical circuit is open or closed. It allows control over current flow.

3. Fuses are important for the safe use of electricity in the home. Find out what fuses are and how they work.

    A fuse is a thin piece of wire designed to carry a limited electrical current. If you try to pass a higher current through the wire, it will heat up so much that it burns or melts. When it melts, it breaks the circuit it is fitted to and stops the current flowing.

4. Draw a circuit diagram for a circuit containing two light bulbs in parallel, a battery and a switch. If one light bulb blows, what happens to the other light bulb? Why?

    If one bulb goes out, the other bulb is unaffected as current still flows through the other bulb.

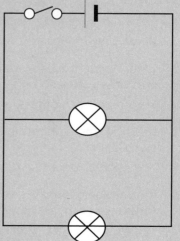

Learning Outcome

8. Research and discuss the ethical and sustainability issues that arise from our generation and consumption of electricity.

 By the end of this chapter you should:
  - appreciate the production of electricity and compare the effects of different methods of this production
  - evaluate our personal contribution to negative effects of electricity production

Electricity is generated in many ways, as shown in the diagram below.

The way we generate electricity raises **ethical** and **sustainability** issues.

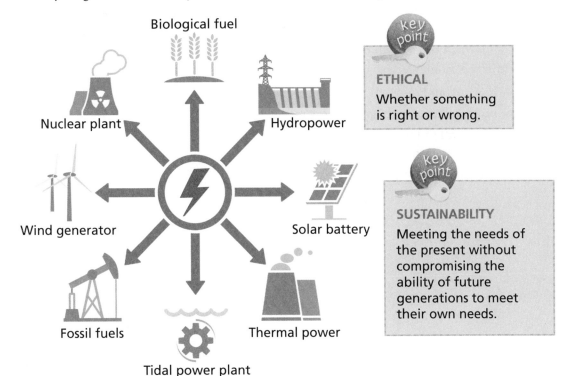

Ways to generate electricity

Ethical Issues	Sustainability Issues
Should we install turbines in scenic areas?	Environmental sustainability
Should we use nuclear power to generate electricity?	Social sustainability
Should we mine for coal?	Economic sustainability

Electricity Consumption

- The more electricity we use, the more electricity that needs to be generated.
- As a result, the majority of greenhouse gas emissions are produced in the developed world.
- The amount of electricity being used has a direct correlation with the amount of CO_2 being emitted.

Our Responsibility for the Future

Our responsibilities:

- Generate electricity in an economical way.
- Develop more sustainable technologies to generate electricity.
- Reduce our consumption of electricity.

Ways in which we can reduce our consumption of electricity at home:

- Insulate our houses.
- Buy appliances with an A energy rating.
- Wait until dishwashers and washing machines are full before using them.
- Hang out washing to dry instead of using a tumble dryer.

exam focus

Make sure you know how you can affect electricity use positively in the future.

Sample Questions

Section A

1. Why do you think some people protest against the construction of wind farms in their community?

   They are not nice to look at.

2. Identify some ways in which people can reduce electricity consumption at home.

   Turn off devices when not in use.

   Use LED lights.

Section B

1. Do you think that generating electricity in wind farms is environmentally sustainable, socially sustainable, and economically sustainable? Give reasons to support your views.

   Environmentally: Yes, because it produces no pollution.

   Socially: Yes, once people begin to see the benefits and if they are spaced out in a region.

   Economically: No, as they are dependent on wind which cannot be relied upon.

2. Do you think it is ethical to generate electricity using wind farms? Justify your answer.

   Yes, as it is better for the environment.

3. What are the advantages of using coal as a fuel?

   It is an efficient and predictable energy source.

4. List the substances produced when coal is burned. How do these substances affect the environment?

   Carbon dioxide: Increases greenhouse gases, warming the Earth.

   Sulphur dioxide: Can cause acid rain.

   Mercury: May run into rivers and lakes, poisoning the habitat for animals.

37 Electronics

Learning Outcomes

4. Research and discuss a technological application of physics in terms of scientific, societal and environmental impact.
5. Design and build simple electronic circuits.

 By the end of this chapter you should:
- develop further an understanding of electronic circuits
- explore the effects and uses of different electronic circuit devices

There are three phases within an electronic circuit:
1. Input
2. Process
3. Output

As circuits become more complex, different inputs are detected by **sensors**, giving many more options for outputs.

Resistors

Resistors are used to control the flow of current in a circuit.
- They are used to protect the more complex electronic components from having too much current flow through them and damaging them.

Light dependent resistor (LDR) – vary the amount of current that can pass through them depending on the amount of light shining on them.
- When there is very little light, the resistance is high and very little current can pass through.
- When there is a lot of light, the resistance is low and they conduct electricity well.
- They are used for: detecting light levels in cameras, turning street lights on in darkness, adjusting screen brightness automatically.

Thermistor   Light Dependent Resistor (LDR)

Circuit diagram symbols for thermistors and light dependent resistors

Thermistors – vary the amount of current that can pass through them depending on their temperature.

- They are used in circuits for digital thermometers, systems to warn drivers their engines are overheating, turning off the kettle when water is boiling and controlling house temperature.

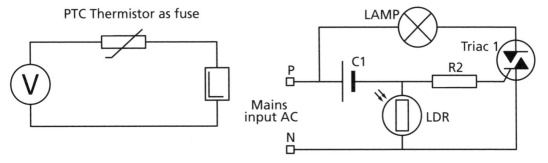

Diodes

Diodes are electronic components that only allow current to flow through them in one direction.

- This is important as electronic components can be damaged by current flowing in the wrong direction.
- **Forward bias:** When diodes are connected in a way that allows current to flow.
- **Reverse bias:** When diodes are connected in a way that does not allow current to flow.
- Diodes have a positive and negative end.

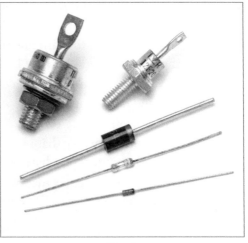

Diodes

NOTE:
Electrons flow from the negative terminal to the positive terminal. However, current is said to flow from positive to negative.
- This is because circuit diagrams were used before scientists understood how electricity worked.
Therefore, a diode in forward bias in a circuit is arranged so that the arrow points away from the positive terminal towards the negative terminal.

Forward bias vs reverse bias circuit diagram:

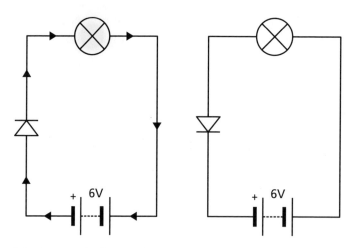

Light Emitting Diodes

Light Emitting Diodes light up when the current is flowing through them.

- Must be connected in forward bias in a circuit to allow the current to flow and the LEDs to light up.
- Contain resistors to stop too much current flowing into them and damaging them.

An LED has two 'legs':

- Positive leg: the longer leg that must be connected to the positive terminal on a battery or power pack.
- Negative leg: the shorter leg that must connect to the negative terminal. Can be identified as the side of the LED closest to it is flattened.

Top view

a = anode (+)
c = cathode (−)

Light Emitting Diode (LED)

Benefits:

- Use a lot less energy than light bulbs.
- Do not get as hot as light bulbs and so last longer.

Uses: Television, car lights, Christmas lights.

Exam Paper 2019

Question 12

When green light is shone into a red solution, such as blood, some of the light is absorbed, some is reflected and some passes straight through.

A student set up the apparatus shown right to investigate the relationship between the concentration of a red solution and how much green light passes through it.

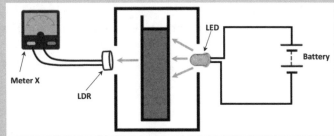

On one side of the test tube of red solution, green light was emitted from a light emitting diode (LED).

On the other side of the test tube, a light dependent resistor (LDR) was used to detect how much green light passed through the solution.

The student made different concentrations of a solution of red food dye by varying the number of drops of dye added to 20 cm³ of water. The resistance of the LDR was then determined using meter X. The following results were obtained.

Number of drops of food colouring	0	1	2	3	4	5	6	7	8
Resistance (Ω)	1.0	1.5	2.0	2.5	3.0	3.5	4.0	4.5	5.0

(a) In the space below, draw a graph of the results obtained.

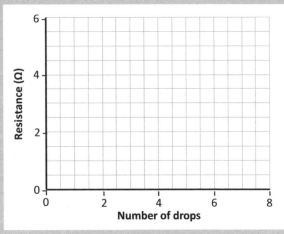

Points plotted (9 × 1). *Correct (straight) line drawn.* (3)

(b) State one conclusion which is supported by the results.
Resistance increases with number of drops/concentration. (3)

(c) Name meter X, which was used to determine the resistance of the LDR.
Ohmmeter. (3)

(d) Name a piece of equipment the student could have used to accurately measure 20 cm³ of water.
Pipette. (3)

(e) A smart watch uses a green LED to measure a person's pulse by shining green light into the red blood in the person's wrist.
Describe one other technological application of physics that is used in everyday life.
Scanners at the supermarket. (3)

Sample Questions

Section A

1. What happens to the resistance of a light dependent resistor (LDR) when light is shone on it?
The resistance in the circuit increases.

2. How can one identify the positive leg and the negative leg of an LED?
Longer leg = positive.
Shorter leg = negative.

3. Describe forward bias and reverse bias.
The forward bias decreases the resistance of the diode whereas the reverse bias increases the resistance of the diode.

Section B

1. How do diodes work?
Current passing through a diode can only go in one direction, called the forward direction. Current trying to flow in the reverse direction is blocked. They are like valves of electronics.

2. Where are LEDs used? What advantages of using LEDs are there? What disadvantages may there be?
Illuminate more cheaply as use less electricity. However, they may have a high initial price.

⇨ **Learning Outcome**

4. Research and discuss a technological application of physics in terms of scientific, societal and environmental impact.

 By the end of this chapter you should:
- consider the impact of technology on science, society and the environment

Technology is the use of scientific knowledge to provide solutions to practical problems or the invention of useful things to solve problems.

Consider the impact of technology on:
Science, society, the environment.

Technology in Food Production

- Farming machinery.
- Processed meats.
- Food transportation.
- Milking parlours/animal sheds.
- Refrigerated storage.
- Ready-made meals and energy drinks.

The tractor is an example of technology in food production

Technology in Transport

- Memory foam for comfortable shoes.
- Power steering and braking systems in cars make them easier to drive.
- Airbags, safety bars, seatbelts and shatter-resistant glass make cars safer.
- More energy efficient cars/boats/planes.

Technology in Energy Use

- LEDs use less power than traditional bulbs.
- Washing machines/dishwashers use less water.
- Cars that run on both fuel and battery power consume less fuel.
- Renewable energy sources.
- New building methods make homes more energy efficient.

Solar panels on roofs

Technology in Communication

- Machines sort post in postal offices.
- The internet is an important tool for communication.
- Computers/smart phones/tablets store, process and send information.
- Satellites send information over long distances.
- Computers are now smaller and easily accessible.

Technology in Medicine

- MRIs are used to make clear images of inside the body.
- Drips deliver a controlled dose of medication.
- New and improved materials are used for stitches, dressings, etc.
- Keyhole surgery allows doctors to treat patients in a less invasive way.

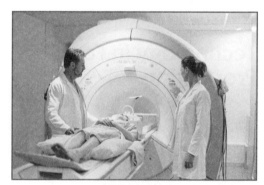

An MRI machine

Nanotechnology

Nanotechnology is the study and use of matter on extremely small scales.
- Used in chemistry, biology, physics and engineering.
- A single sheet of newspaper is approximately 100,000 nanometres thick.

Uses:
- Sunscreens that contain nanoparticles of zinc oxide or titanium oxide, which absorb more easily into the skin.
- Car paint and eyeglass lenses use nanoparticles of aluminium silicate to increase their scratch resistance.
- Computers use nanoscale transistors, which allow computers to become smaller.

Technology and Sustainability

- Solar and wind energy.
- More efficient cars, homes and appliances.
- Nanotechnology used to make more efficient solar panels, engines and batteries.
- Bioplastics that break down in nature have been developed to replace non-biodegradable plastics.

Be able to describe how technology can influence sustainability.

Sample Questions

Section A

1. List 3 technologies that you use.

   Phone, TV and drone.

2. List 3 technologies used in your home.

   Laptops, communication technology and video camera.

3. List 3 technologies used in your school.

   Social networking, online teaching, interactive whiteboards and mobile devices.

Section B

1. Choose two technologies that you think society would struggle to cope without and explain your choice.

   Phone: People are reliant on constant communication and web-based data.

   Transport: It would be hard to get goods from A to B without proper transport. So much of our commerce is based on worldwide transport.

2. Choose a technology and outline major changes that have occurred in its development.

   Phone: Since its inception it has gone from local to international to worldwide and cord phones to mobile.

3. Choose one technology used in medicine that you think is very important. Give clear reasons for your choice.

   Robotic surgery allows precision without mistakes due to fatigue.